MW00654640

Without Delay

A RECIPE FOR SAFETY, OPERATIONS AND
MAINTENANCE EXCELLENCE

Simon Lane

Melbourne, Australia

Copyright © 2022 by Simon Lane.

All rights reserved. No part of this publication may be reproduced, distributed or transmitted in any form or by any means, including photocopying, recording, or other electronic or mechanical methods, without the prior written permission of the publisher, except in the case of brief quotations embodied in critical reviews and certain other noncommercial uses permitted by copyright law. For permission requests, write to the publisher, addressed "Attention: Permissions Coordinator," at the address below.

Simon Lane C/- Intertype Publish and Print
Unit 45, 125 Highbury Road
BURWOOD VIC 3125
www.intertype.com.au

Ordering Information:
Quantity sales. Special discounts are available on quantity purchases by corporations, associations, and others. For details, contact the "Special Sales Department" at the address above.

Without Delay/ Simon Lane. —1st ed.
ISBN 978-0-6454140-8-0

Contents

To the memory of my parents and to my three children: Megan, Honor and Owen

Acknowledgements

On my last day with SBS Transit Rail in September 2017 Leong Yim Sing, my successor as 'Head of Rail at SBS Transit Rail, suggested to me that I should write a book, to share my reflections and the lessons learned over a 40 year career, to assist other rail managers with their own learning and reflections.

I have worked with so many wonderful colleagues through the years, but a few have significantly stimulated my thinking and working methods. They include, from my Ipswich days, Graham Eccles, from my Swansea days, Alison Forster and from ScotRail times, Alan Chaplin, George Barclay and Cyril Bleasdale. From Melbourne, Norm Grady, John Barry, Craig Sparrius and Dr Jackie Graham. From Sydney, Klaus Clemens, Ron Creighton, Arthur Smith and Vivienne King. From Singapore, T C Chew, Sim Wee Meng, Chua Chong Kheng, Wong Wai Keong and my fellow travellers on the SBS Transit Rail reliability transformation particularly Foo Jang Kae, Michael Harrison, Alex Goie, Leong Yim Sing, Francis Yap and more than anyone else, Jeffrey Sim who brought ambition, technical capability, and energy to the team.

My career and the lessons learned owe the 'giants' named in the acknowledgements above a great deal. As Sir Isaac Newton said, "If I have seen further than the rest it is because I have stood on the shoulder of giants".

I would also like to thank Professor Graham Currie for Public Transport at Monash University in Melbourne, Professor Peter Newman for Sustainability at Curtin University in Perth, WA and Ian Horseman-Sewell, Managing Director of First Class Partnerships, London for their guidance and advice.

More than anyone else, however, without my partner Susie Buckie's encouragement, patience, guidance, editorial reviews and support this book would never have seen the light of day.

Setting the Scene: An Underperforming Industry

*S*ir Isaac Newton apparently said 'that if I have seen further than the
rest it is because I have stood on the shoulders of giants'. This book's
intent is that the readers will be able to quickly stand on the shoulders of giants passed and deliver incredible outcomes for the communities
that their railways serve.

Starting Out

In 1986, after three consecutive awful evening peaks for passengers travelling from London Victoria's Station to Epsom Downs another set of cancellations plagued the line again. There were about 2000 angry passengers on the concourse, many who had been providing clear, unambiguous feedback to the young Duty Manager. When a train eventually arrived to take them home, the Duty Manager asked a couple of passengers in one carriage to get off so he could board the train.

He called for attention, gave his name and position and explained that he and his staff were equally frustrated with the dreadful service, that it represented a management problem that would be resolved, he assured them before apologizing once again. There was a short, silent pause before the carriage, slowly at first then loudly and involving almost everybody, applauded the Manager. He went on to each carriage in turn with the same response.

He had had enough of watching the dreadful performance repeat itself and resolved to do something about it. The next day the leading letter in London's Evening Standard, entitled The Soothing Voice in Victoria's Crush Hour praised the fact that somebody, somewhere cared. The Duty Manager had crossed a line – he had internalised that O&M Managers had to take personal responsibility for poor performance and become proactive and do something about it.

The LONDON STANDARD, MONDAY, NOVEMBER 24, 1986—17

THE CHANCE TO AIR YOUR VIEWS

A soothing voice in Victoria's crush hour

What I recall from the letter were the comments that 'it hadn't got them home any earlier but they knew that somewhere somebody really cared'.

I was that Duty Manager. Throughout my career since then I have sought to identify the underlying causes of poor reliability and to deal with them. This book sheds light on many of the lessons learned over a 40 year journey and provides a reference for interested Managers, specifically providing insights that were not taught but would have helped a lot if they had been through my career.

My Final Position

At the end of my career, in Singapore with SBS Transit in 2015, a review of 41 previous delays over 5 minutes through 2014 and 2015 revealed that, with the exception of 3 delays, the others had all been caused by risk factors which were well known. In that sense we had failed in our obligation to proactively identify and mitigate risk. Subsequently we set ourselves a goal of eliminating all delays caused by known risk factors by rigorous, systematic analysis of performance, the identification of consequential risks and challenges and their mitigation. From 21 delays over 5 minutes per year they have gone to 2 or less delays over 5 minutes for several years.

For new major projects, working as a project reviewer and evaluator I have developed a logic based decision tree framework to test the underlying completeness and maturity of the Business Case. What emerges is a new tendency for what I call 'trophy projects' where much cheaper, higher value options are not even considered forcing the case that the only viable solution is a new city center tunnel with new stations and platforms.

The option analysis in the Business Cases, when publicly available, tend to be very poor. Options chosen for evaluation, often leaving out realistic alternatives, tend to resemble a sketch by the British comedians The Goodies where, in Noshos Dog Food the dog food advertiser offers the dog wood chips, nails or dog meat, the result being a celebration when the hungry dog selects the dog food.

Another book, currently being written, called Missing Our Transport Challenges will provide detail looking at flawed projects in Sydney and Melbourne in Australia and Toronto in Canada, contrasting with great strategy and delivery by Singapore's Land Transport Authority.

Consultants have become trapped by this prevailing 'Groupthink' too, being asked to prepare analysis and advice to support pre-determined outcomes under the silent threat of not being asked to conduct future work if their advice is not in line with the required outcome. You don't think this happens? It happens a lot. Missing Our Transport Challenges will provide many case studies.

Who is this book aimed at?

This book is aimed at Operations and Maintenance (O&M) Managers, Rail Planners and Regulators but could also be useful for other industries and organisations.

It reflects the key learnings and reflections between the mid-1980s and 2022.

The aim is to enable the reader, in time to have a stronger base from which to build professional excellence. The perspective throughout the book, in each Part and chapter is as follows:

- Career Observations

- Consequential Insights
- I later read this which reinforced my thinking and practice
- If I was starting again, I would adopt this approach.

My claim is that if you choose to adopt the thinking outlined and to implement some or many of the ideas contained here, it is highly likely that the railway you are involved with will perform at a much higher level and with a much higher level of predictability and assurance than has been the case until now.

The value to passengers, employees, owners and managers will increase, perhaps in a way that is as yet deemed as being impossible.

Career highlights emerged from being a Duty Manager at Victoria Station in London, an Area Manager in Swansea in UK, Head of Operations for Sco-tRail in UK, Managing Director of Melbourne's Network, CEO of Sydney's Network including the Sydney 2000 Olympic Rail task, in Singapore as Head of SBS Transit's Metro Rail Business and later as a consultant.

Why have I decided to write this?

The industry has generally failed to deliver. This book tries to provide a context and explanation of key things I have learned along the way which I wish I had not had to learn for myself, which might help to accelerate yours, and others, professional life's learnings for the industry's benefit.

This book attempts to provide a reference, section by section of key lessons learned on my journey. The hope is that it will assist some managers to deepen their understanding of the challenges and equip them to achieve much higher performance.

With the notable exception of Hong Kong's MTRC and more recently Singapore's Operators, Sydney Trains and Perth's PTA almost all railways where I have worked or have good knowledge of have failed their customers, their owners and funders over a long period of time.

Frequent service failures, prohibitively protective work practices, poorly considered and very expensive new projects are normal and accepted.

O&M Managers are generally untrained outside their particular silo and are, consequently, incompetent. This lack of contemporary management skill training explains why so many are unable to demonstrate that they understand performance in a statistically valid way, generally have no list of risks and challengers or resourced mitigation plans – basic O&M management requirements.

Acceptance of poor performance seems to be ingrained and accepted, associated with a fashionable focus on process rather than outcomes. This focus seems to slow down decision making and creates an inertia associated with risk aversion which slows down decision making and stifles initiative. All undesirable.

The Question of Culpability

Later in the book the question of Management Culpability is considered within a three culture model which looks at the characteristics and examples of Denial or Professional Recklessness, Administrative or Professional Negligence and High Performance.

High Performance cultures and O&M Organisations have distinct characteristics. These include the following:

- Uncontrolled events are very rare including accidents, loss of asset availability, delays, or non compliance with Procedures
- Uncontrolled events, which are really loss of management control events (delays, accidents, near misses), are found to be almost unforeseeable with no precursor events.
- Investigations into loss of control events (delays, accidents etc) are deep with well considered preventative actions planned and implemented.
- A strong approach to proactive risk identification and mitigation is embedded.

Unfortunately, these characteristics are rare in Rail O&M organisations.

My Beginning

On my 12-year career journey from London to Swansea and Scotland before my 26-year swing which took me twice through Melbourne, Sydney and Singapore I have enjoyed a journey of continuous learning, analysing and questioning the underlying reasons for failures of both service delivery and the management of the task. On reflection I have encountered many areas where the industry has generally failed to deliver very good value to the community with only a few notable exceptions.

In 1982 I got close to winning a Management Trainee's job with Procter and Gamble whose booklet highlighted 'that there is always a better way' something that resonated strongly with me. I have taken that message with me all my working life. When Sir Walter Scott said that 'anything is possible if we think it is' he was expressing a perspective that was more Procter and Gamble than British Rail. Unfortunately, I have found that in the railway industry 'don't stick your neck out' is much more prevalent.

In recent years I have tried to identify the key factors which have led to this underperformance and, perhaps more importantly, where the cultural, skill and knowledge gaps occur to make these outcomes likely.

In a general sense I find that it is not about commitment or desire amongst supervisors and front line managers since almost all the people I have worked with, particularly the 'lifers' as I call them, those who have worked in the industry all their lives, have been loyal and dedicated. As with the findings of the 1987 Zeebrugge capsizing of a Cross Channel Ferry and with the 1988 Clapham Train Crash while 'at first sight the faults which led to the disaster were the errors of front line staff and supervisors a full investigation led inexorably to the conclusion that the underlying faults lay higher up the company'.

In the investigation into the 1988 explosion of the Piper Alpha oil platform in the UK's North Sea Lord Cullen observed that management going through the motions, being easily satisfied that things were well was widespread. He also stated that 'any unexpected failure or delay is evidence of a failure of management; of failure to having identified the risk factors and/or having failed to mitigate those risks'. This has a compelling logic to it – almost all of the reliability, asset condition and competence problems in rail are, I believe almost all of the reliability, asset condition and competence problems in rail are due to management failures, failures to be aware and/or failures to be proactive in mitigating the risks. Hence the question of culpability needs to be raised.

If this is the case, what are the underlying causes? I have concluded that there are six key issues:

- Working in a protected, semi monopolistic environment where more competition/rivalry would motivate O&M managers to achieve much higher performance at lower costs.

- A stubborn reluctance of senior managers to consider whether 'the normal' was as good as could reasonably be delivered. I have come to see a stubborn determination by decision makers and senior managers not to want to learn from the mistakes of the past or from similar industries.

- A lack of knowledge that Railways require an appreciation and understanding of a complete system. The industry has many subject experts within their silo but little across the whole system.

- The amateurish 'good bloke' theory of management is alive and well, even with women.

- A combination of an easy acceptance that things are generally OK and a lack of application of a disciplined management review mechanism where close enough is good enough.

- A lack of interest in searching for applicable lessons from both within Rail and from industries with similar challenges. This reflects itself in a low ability and willingness to learn and to do much better.

Crucially, most of what I write about here reflects my learning and things that, in retrospect, I should not have had to learn for myself. My own learning, built on a continuous questioning and analysis of 'why is it like this and why can't performance be much better?', I found much later to be borne out by academic studies which I reference in the relevant section.

Over the years I have concluded that the industry's underperformance is no one's fault but our own. Why can't urban rail systems be as reliable as other critical social network services such as electricity and water? In 2015, with a talented team of people in Singapore we embarked on an experiment to see if it was possible and found it was not only possible but sustainable too.

For each part and chapter of this book, I have sought to provide an explanation of why I have selected this as an area of focus, along with some background and experience which you, as the reader can shape into recommendations or areas of reflection for yourself. The sections can be read and considered in any order. The elements are outlined below:

Six Parts

Part One explores the seven foundations of High-Performance O&M Organisational capability and cultures. It considers the importance of Appetite, Guiding Principles for prioritization and focus, the qualifications and experience of senior managers, Governance and how to best enable multiple levels of leadership to make what was regarded as impossible, possible.

Part Two considers the six universal obligations of O&M Management. These obligations emerge from the Health and Safety Legislation in every jurisdiction from North America to the UK, Singapore, and Australia yet this book reveals how poorly managers are aware of and capable to meet them. It also looks at the Untrained Industry which has embedded a low level of Management Competence which makes meeting their universal obligations so difficult whilst also providing reference as to 'what good looks like'.

Part Three explores common features of Organisational Cultures from Denial/Professional Recklessness to Administrative/Professional Negligence and High Performance. It also considers the 'normalisation of deviance' within O&M Organisations and its causes.

Part Four considers The Operator's Challenge in keeping the interfaces between Assets and Systems, Operating Rules and Procedures and Competent People including Modification Control tight and healthy. This section considers 26 specific risks that O&M Managers need to be aware of and to manage proactively and provides good practice examples in respect to each risk.

Part Five looks at the complementary roles of the Owner of a Network and the O&M Manager in light of the creeping trend of the Owner to micro manage and direct franchises leaving accountability increasingly unclear. It identifies lessons learnt from the various models in the UK, Singapore and Australia and their impact on enabling high performance to be encouraged, or not. It also considers the legal obligation of private sector Boards to act in the interest of their shareholders rather than the long term good of the railway and the consequential gap that needs to be filled by the Owner or State Authority, something that is often left open.

Part Six provides two complementary Frameworks for increasing network capacity and also a major project planning and assessment Logic Tree. Unfortunately, it identifies a trend of Rail Planners and Politicians to use a reversed logic in an attempt to justify decisions and announcements made before any analysis of options was considered. Of the eight steps in the Logic Tree it is common for projects planning to start with step seven being decided first.

It also provides an overview of Operational Readiness Requirements which seems to have dogged many high profile projects notable Crossrail in the UK. It highlights how the use of a defined Operational Requirement Framework helps all parties to align in delivering a high quality outcome for all stakeholders and emphasises that the earliest this is prepared in either the procurement or project phase the better.

Reflections

As a result of these reflections, I concluded that the critical aspects of effective safety management were the same as those that characterised reliability excellence became evident.

Our job as O&M managers is to pre-empt and avoid unplanned events, by understanding and studying drivers of system and people's performance, to identifying vulnerability and risk, and to intervene accordingly. While the challenges are often seen as largely technical, it is evident that the greatest challenges are cultural and that as a leader you are primarily a helper, a coach, an enabler.

In many developed countries including Singapore and the UK, through the Health and Safety legislation, managers are required to take all reasonable steps to avoid loss of control events, to reduce the risks to As Low As Reasonably Practicable (ALARP), but to do that requires entrenched knowledge and capability. In Australia however, section 46 of the Rail Safety National

Legislation requires duty holders to reduce risk to So Far As Is Reasonably Practical (SFAIRP). So, what is the difference and why is it important?

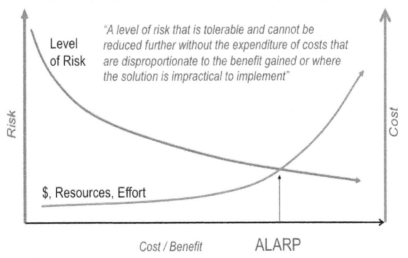

Level of Risk

"A level of risk that is tolerable and cannot be reduced further without the expenditure of costs that are disproportionate to the benefit gained or where the solution is impractical to implement"

$, Resources, Effort

Cost / Benefit   ALARP

While this book recognises that while the overall risk in a given situation may be at the ALARP level, an untreated risk may remain that can be mitigated without disproportionate effort. As Richard Robinson argues in his article "Near Enough Not Safe Enough" in the January 2014 edition of Engineers Australia "…it does not matter how low the risk estimate is, if more can be done for very little effort, then the failure to do so will be negligent in the event of an incident. That subtle difference challenges Rail O&M managers to take more action if more can be done with little effort even if the ALARP requirement has been achieved. The legal nuance hinges on the interpretation of what is 'reasonably practicable'. The SBS Transit Rail reliability transformation effectively adopted a SFAIRP rather than the more traditional ALARP approach. If something could be done with relatively little effort or cost, then it was done.

It is well known that Losing Control through delays or accidents disrupts service delivery, the cost of recovery being both disruptive and expensive, leaving aside any loss of productivity as a consequence, highlighting the requirement to strive to avoid these events, particularly when so many loss of control events are foreseeable. As it is with safety and 'near enough not safe enough' so it is with reliability and both operational and asset performance and condition.

It is also well known that effective management does not wait for an injury, an accident, or a delay to occur before managers act. Since these 'loss of control' events usually have precursor events why haven't managers acted? What stops them? Usually themselves. Curious, eh?

By 2018, after a second spell with SBS Transit Rail that it is possible to operate a safety incident and delay free railway had been proven. 'That anything is possible if we think it is' had come to pass. By 2020 SBS Transit's Metro lines both achieved a Mean number of train km between delays over 5 minutes (MKBF) over 2.0 million with two Lines operating with two or less delays over 5 minutes per year.

I found that it is the Business Rhythm that provides the glue, the mechanism for bringing an ambitious mission to life with disciplined systems thinking for monitoring and empowering the organisation resulting in multiple levels of aligned leadership leading to delivering those 'impossible' outcomes on a sustained basis.

I have concluded that the difference between poor performance and excellence lies with the capability of the Senior Leadership Group to apply rigorous systems thinking with sufficient discipline and appetite to unleash the latent capacity of their staff.

Disclaimer

1. This book outlines by reflections and retrospective lessons. The intent is to provide points of reflection for the reader. Where it appears to be critical it is only where I believe that an important point of learning emerges. In the same way that I have not listed my errors and omissions I have also tried to ensure that the reputations of others are not damaged.

2. The book is not comprehensive. Indeed, others may find that they do not agree with my reflections or believe that I have missed out important points. I will welcome any feedback. If the book prompts a discussion that is for the good.

3. I think I would have liked to have been able to read this type of book at different stages of my career, not as a template but as a point of reference and reflection. I haven't seen or heard of a book of this nature. It might prompt others to enrichen the field – let's hope so.

4. I would be grateful for notification of any corrections that should be incorporated in future reprints or editions of this book.

Simon Lane, 2022

PART ONE: The Foundations of O&M Excellence

This part of the book seeks to bring out key attributes of what a high performing O&M Organisation looks like.

The various attributes here are non-technical in their nature in respect to O&M Management but are prerequisites for high performance.

CHAPTER ONE

The importance of Appetite for Excellence

I came to believe that appetite is the most important ingredient of all regarding high safety, reliability, asset management and competence performance. I have concluded that Sir Walter Scott was correct in claiming 'that anything is possible if we think it is'.

As JFK said, 'If not us, who? If not now, when? As he challenged the US Agencies to land a man on the moon before the 1960s had ended, when the 'how' was both unknown and unproven.

Certainly, the experience we had in the State Rail Authority for the Sydney Olympic Rail Task, in SBS Transit for the start up of the North East Line and again with SBS Transit for the reliability revolution from 2015 suggest that Sir Walter Scott was correct, that 'anything is possible if we think it is.'. In each example the collective ambition, buy in, discipline and rigor from hundreds of people at multiple levels in those organisations delivered outcomes which wildly surpassed the external stakeholders' expectations.

Conversely, with a lack of appetite, poor and mediocre performance prevails when allowed.

Career Observations

In 2019, when conducting a review of the reliability problems facing a major commuter railway, all day punctuality of 92% and a peak hours reliability under 85% then delivering 95% within 5 minutes in the peak looks impossible to the senior management team even though the key supervisors and front line staff knew it is possible because they used to do it and there was a well publicised plan to get there only five years previously. This organisation had given up on delivering a level of performance which was above the minimum requirements. Such a compliance culture rather than high performance is common.

A GoA 4 or UTS system performed at an average MKBF of 40k for many years and was said by the CEO in 2017 to be at its limit and a major renewal would be necessary to do any better. A change in management created a set of internal processes and management systems that delivered an MKBF over 250k four years later. How about that?

Looking back it is almost always the case that delays over 5 minutes are almost always caused by issues and vulnerabilities which are well known within O&M organisations but that the management had either chosen not to behave proactively or was unaware of how and where to look. Low appetite and low skill levels are common.

What also stands out throughout my career is that, unless there was a Special Cause event (more of that later) which created obvious delays the same trains are late almost every day, reflecting the entrenched patterns of either poor timetable design, poor operating discipline, or both.

Without a Special Cause event peak hour reliability in suburban networks seem to hover between 85% and 90%. That the same repeating patterns of late running delay so many people doesn't seem to be of much interest. Mediocrity is widely accepted.

UK Experience 1980s

As a young Traffic Manager, I was told that the early weeks of Ipswich electrification would be very unreliable. It was 'how things are'. With Graham Eccles and our supervisory team, we ensured that it went almost perfectly from day one. It required a rigorous assessment of every step in the delivery of the timetable to identify risks and resource gaps and to mitigate and close the gaps. Really, it was the least we could have done but it was seen as overly ambitious by many.

In my career as a Duty Station Manager at London's Victoria Station in 1985/87 the senior managers and the prevailing senior management culture was openly oppositional to the idea that performance outcomes could and should be much better. At Victoria I had found entrenched bias against a desire to do much better, a lack or no understanding of variation and a lack of openness to learn and a general lack of ambition so, in frustration, I left the industry.

I missed the social value that railways bring their cities and had the opportunity to return after 18 months but in a much more senior position where the opportunity to shape and implement change presented itself. Thanks to Chris Daughton my old Area Manager from Victoria, but the Western Regional Personnel Head in 1988.

Sydney Olympics Rail Task 2000

In 1996, while still working in Melbourne, an industry leader stated that the Sydney Olympic Rail Task would be unsuccessful in its aims, that it was undeliverable. In December 1997 I was appointed CEO of the State Rail Authority. We turned our collective minds to the task. We achieved it proving the so called experts, and the media, wrong.

The Sydney 2000 Olympic Rail Task: A Gold Medal Performance

- 1000 days of planning, testing and verifying plans
- Fleet Utlisation over 98%
- 'I am proud to wear their uniform in the streets'
- Making much more than the sum of the parts
- 'It was like being part of a football team that finally fulfilled its potential after years of criticism'
- 'They have done us and our city proud'

Daily Telegraph

Saturday, September 23, 2000

Prophets of doom got it all wrong

SUPER Friday, the day which promised the most thrilling competition of the Games, and marked the beginning of the track and field program, also promised the biggest influx yet of Olympic fans to Homebush.

So Super Friday could also have been the day of super chaos for Sydney's rail transport system.

But the prophets of doom — those who foretold a day of reckoning when the rail system would be tested to the point of failure by sheer weight of numbers — were proved wrong. By 4pm yesterday, more than 200,000 people had travelled by rail to Homebush and, while there were some delays, the massive uplift ran astonishingly smoothly. What was described by Premier Bob Carr — with perhaps a hint of hyperbole — as an exercise "bigger than D-day" had been carried off with great success.

Before the Games began, a series of disconcerting problems with the city rail — serial derailments, timetabling hitches, cancelled services and signal failures the most serious — had given rise to a not-unreasonable level of anxiety about the capacity of the system to cope during the great carnival.

And, while we still have "super Saturday and super Sunday" to negotiate — in fact, we still have nine days of testing Olympic conditions — it appears the system is coping admirably.

Significantly, Olympic commuters have sung the praises of rail staff, both on the trains and at stations, for their helpful and efficient manner and for their friendly demeanour. The careful arrangement of pedestrian traffic flows at stations — at Central station most notably — has also resulted in swift and painless progress through ticket barriers — for which passengers have been grateful.

CityRail staff are regularly criticised by disgruntled passengers, who are wont to blame them unreasonably for all rail problems — from vandalism, to late-running services to fare increases — and understandably, they are immune to it.

But it is to be hoped they are not now so hardened by that experience that they are deaf to praise as well. Today, the employees of CityRail, the people who have manned ticket booths, operated checkpoints, directed streams of travellers unfamiliar with our city, dealt with a thousand different problems every Olympic day, may take a bow.

They have done us and our city proud.

---

of over 98% for about a month covering both the Olympic and Paralympic Games. When this utilisation was first identified it was deemed to be an impossible task but over three stages the Rolling Stock team identified a pathway, the risks and the resource requirements to deliver it. The senior team's role was to test and verify their assumptions and logic, to provide the resources and to cheer loudly from the sideline.

It reminds me of a saying by the composer Leonard Bernstein that 'to do great things two conditions are needed: A plan and not quite enough time'. The Olympics was a bit like that.

Singapore Rail 2015 to 2020

When asked by senior colleagues in SBS Transit Rail in mid-2015 about what we could achieve in five years I said that I wanted to knock MTR off its reliability perch which I repeated at a UITP meeting in Singapore in 2016. I was told by a senior SBS Transit Rail colleague on both occasions that I sounded ridiculous.

We had no roadmap but felt we could achieve it because so many of the causes of delays over 5 minutes were well known to us. An industry leader commented that it was not achievable, and if

it was, then it was not sustainable, even though the MKBF in MTR in Hong Kong were exceeding 700k at the time.

In 2018 the MKBF rose above 1.0 million for the first time on SBS Transit's Rail North East Line, repeated again in 2019 and achieved over 2.0 million in 2020 and 2021.

Australian Experience

In Australia, separate reviews in recent years for three passenger Operators revealed some serious shortcomings.

In one case, over 100 late or overdue safety management actions were reported to the Board without any concern about the apparent inconsistency with the 'safety is our top priority' mantra, displaying a lack of both commitment to their own policy and standards but also an apparent lack of appetite.

In the others there was a refusal by senior managers to consider whether there were sufficient staff on duty to enable the requirements of Emergency Management Plans at underground stations to be fully implemented or whether those staff were in a state of high readiness to implement the required actions of the Emergency Management Plans.

In two of those Operators the underlying reliability was very poor when compared to similar organisations and where the reliability causation was staring the management in the face, if only they were willing and able to look and act.

Reflection

In Sydney and with SBS Transit Rail the outcome outperformed the promise. The collective intelligence, insights, experience, discipline and professionalism of the whole body corporate delivered.

In each case there was no clear roadmap but an appetite and ambition to deliver an outcome which was perceived as being impossible. Where there were no external factors which would prevent its delivery, the task was to find a way.

I came to understand that, consequently:

That it is possible to avoid all foreseeable delays and incidents attributable to known areas of risk if you have the appetite for it. Without that desire mediocrity prevails.

ScotRail

Having decided that what had become seen as tolerable was sufficient we embarked on a disciplined process of seeking to improve the precise execution of the Train Plan while also identifying where it was inoperable with the infrastructure layout.

What we discovered was that the so-called regular events that prevented good performance were not the major contributors at all and that there were many controllables where we could act.

In The Guardian on December 10th 1992, under an article titled Flying ScotRail beats passenger charter 'on-time' targets I was quoted as saying that 'people get used to trains being late, and so do the managers. This is not right and we are doing something about it'. Primarily, those 'people' were our managers

As I found later in Melbourne in the mid 1990s the managers were keen to do better, something which required a review of the possible and a commitment to the passengers. This required an acceptance of the evidence, something which managers in some other systems refused to do later when provided within Independent Review. More of that later.

North East Line, Singapore

In this case colleagues in the senior management team were open to exploring the possibility of trying to operate a Metro line which would never have a delay over 5 minutes, from 21 delays per year over 2 years which was already Singapore's most reliable line in 2014 and 2015.

This group found a way of delivering what they regarded as impossible in 2015 and sustained performance of no more than 2 delays per year from 2018 onwards. The steps we took are outlined in several sections of this book. The SBS Transit Rail reliability transformation after 2015 reflects almost all of the lessons learned in the previous 33 years.

Bukit Panjang LRT, Singapore

In this case the CEO of the holding company and its Managing Director had gone public in 2017 saying that there was nothing that could be done about the reliability challenges which resulted in an MKBF of about 35k per year for many years.

A new, ambitious, highly disciplined and rigorous team went on a journey to explore the underlying patterns of failure, which having mitigated many of the controllable risks resulted in a 12 month moving average MKBF of over 250k in mid 2021.

As with ScotRail, the Olympic Rail task and the North East Line, they made the seemingly impossible, possible.

By contrast, UK Rail

In The Times on 31 December 2017 there was a report on rail reliability which revealed that in the five preceding weeks 48% of suburban trains in the UK had run over five minutes late or long distance trains over ten minutes late.

Only one of the 28 Operators had operated fewer than 33% of their trains being over 5 minutes late. Paul Plummer, CEO of the UK's Rail Delivery Group was reported in the Times as saying that 'our railway performs very well compared to many countries' omitting to say which countries.

Similarly, George Muir's 2021 biography of Bob Reid states that 'punctuality of short distance trains of 90% within 5 minutes of time is good' even though an analysis of suburban railways shows that the 10% of trains are generally the same ones every day. This too was the inertia in Singapore in 2015 with their metro system – a delay over 5 minutes every three weeks on the best performing line, SBS Transit's North East Line was quite acceptable.

More evidence of entrenched negligence or even reckless management. A failure to meet any of Deming's four key functions of profound knowledge which is considered in detail in Part Two in the chapter about understanding performance.

Overall

I concluded that where performance is either exceptional or not, it reflects the appetite of the O&M Manager and even worse, the Network Owner and/or Regulator. Four particular examples come to mind highlighting that our mindset of the possible is often between our ears.

- Roger Bannister and the four minute mile.

Before he became the first person to run a mile in under four minutes many people including doctors considered that it was impossible.

He completed it on May 6th 1954. Eight others did it within 12 months. Not impossible at all.

- Sir Alex Ferguson (SAF) and Manchester United

When SAF was appointed manager of Manchester United in 1986 he said that Manchester United would knock Liverpool off its perch, as the dominant soccer team in the UK. Liverpool had won the league six times in the previous decade and went on to win three more titles in the next four years. SAF sounded ridiculous since Manchester United had not won he league for 19 years.

From 1992/93 Manchester United won 13 titles under his management including seven titles in a decade from 1992/93. SAF Made it possible. During his tenure of 27 seasons his team won more trophies than any other manager in British football ever. A very unlikely prospect in 1986.

- Clean Trains in cold weather in UK, as told by a former colleague from BR days, Adrian Caltieiri.

'A few weeks before takeover Sea Containers were filming dirty coaches at Kings Cross. When Christopher Garnett arrived, he showed the film and of course our BR type response was freezing conditions, unable to use the wash plants etc. 'No', he said 'you just don't have a process to cope with winter'.

He gave us 4 weeks to come up with a solution and we did. Sea Co was happy with the capex and opex as long as they got clean coaches all year round. A step change from BR.

- Train reliability

I met a manager from one of the big train suppliers in Brisbane in 2017 and asked him what level of reliability would he guarantee for new trains for the Australian system. He stated that an MKBF of 200k km was the upper limit.

When I explained that in Singapore SBS Transit had operated a 15 years old fleet for 13 million train km without a Rolling Stock delay he told me that that was impossible, that they must be fiddling the numbers; Not a sense of wonder or a question as to how had they done that.

The power of Groupthink

Groupthink reflects the entrenched culture and thinking habits. As Andrew Haines wrote 'Every morning on far too much of the world's railway networks we get up and expect to fail. It doesn't have to be like that'. I strongly agree.

The Rail O&M industry is dominated by leaders with very conservative mindsets. 'Do not stick your neck out', staying with group think is normal, so is a very high level of uncontrolled, unexpected events resulting in either unreliability, unsafety or both. This reliance on entrenched bias combined with a lack of openness to learning and improving is most concerning.

I later read this which reinforced my thinking and practice

- **Good to Great by Jim Collins**

The first chapter is titled 'Good is the enemy of Great' in which he finds that 'the vast majority of companies never become great precisely because the vast majority become quite good'. They do what is necessary to achieve minimum requirements (profit, growth etc) but then hold back from being as good as they could possibly be.

Throughout my career almost all senior Rail managers have accepted what could only be called ordinary performance. Unfortunately, there seems to be very little evidence of the continual push to do any better in the various privatisation models in the UK or Australia despite the promise of privatisation's sponsors.

It can be done, and often is

Jim Collins introduced to me the term BHAGS; Big, Hairy, Audacious Goals, and explained their importance in setting seemingly impossible goals which high performing teams generally find a way of achieiving. I first came across the use of BHAGs in SBS Transit in 2004 when the SBS Transit Rail team challenged to deliver a target before 2006 that was widely regarded as being impossible.

The challenge for the SBS Transit Rail team in 2004 was not to view the task as being impossible to the extent that it should be ignored, the 'groupthink, stay safe, stay together mindset', but was to challenge ourselves to find a way. It was not a question of whether it was possible but only of how could we do it.

It was similar to the challenge that had faced the Rail team in Sydney in1998, recognising that by doing everything in the proven and established way, the Olympic Rail Task would only have been ready in late2001, not September2000.

Reflections

As with the Olympics in Sydney, in SBS Transit Rail in 2004/05, a way was found. It required a mindset change, to review, challenge and change the approach to almost all areas of the Business that become stronger, more efficient and smarter as a result.

In a sense, the reliability targets we set ourselves in Singapore in2015 was a BHAG, to double the reliability by 2018 of what was already Singapore's most reliable Line. Again, it was achieved with a large margin and set in play a set of processes and practices that have led to further and sustainable improvement.

Rather than Transport Agencies setting Operators 'safe but ordinary' reliability targets reflecting a comfortable groupthink, it would be interesting to see new targets of reliability demanded. High Performing O&M Organisations would almost certainly find a way with others having to leave the market or rapidly catch up.

I believe that almost everybody wants to be part of a mission that achieves something which stakeholders would regard as remarkable and that managers and their teams want to achieve career highlights in the process.

In the examples from Melbourne in the 19990s, the Sydney Olympic Rail Task and the Reliability Transformation to world class with SBS Transit Rail in Singapore in the post 2015 period, having identified the possible pathway to take, and be seen to take 'all reasonable steps' to proactively and systematically identify and mitigate all foreseeable risks, remarkable results followed, not only in terms of measurable outcomes but also with the memories and sense of team.

While some would see the examples of management courage, I would contend that in each case we adopted Du Pont's philosophy that, in each case we got what we demonstrated what we wanted. It is both a philosophical and team commitment.

To those who believe we were courageous I ask, so what else could we have done in each of the circumstances. Our commitment to each other, to our stakeholders and each other demanded it.

If I was starting again, I would adopt this approach.
Have the appetite and ambition to:
- Take on a mission and bring the organisation with you. You can't do it without multiple layers and many people adopting leadership behaviours.

- Take all reasonable steps to proactively and systematically identify and mitigate risks.
- Be courageous and challenge the 'good enough' acceptance.

CHAPTER TWO

Guiding Principles

I came to believe that without established timeless Principles regarding the identification and mitigation of risk, the importance of the customer when making decisions, the responsibility of management to strengthen organisations for their successor's successors and to build the competence, confidence and alignment of the staff often flipped and flopped from one theme to another with relatively poor performance as one of the outcomes.

Before we embarked on the SBS Transit Rail Reliability Transformation I drafted a set of 'universal truths' which I had witnessed, observed and experienced as foundations of a proactive and high performance culture during my career. I believed it was essential to discuss, agree and internalise these 'truths' with the senior management team if we were going to be able to achieve a sustainable change.

The senior Rail team wanted to be clear about those truths before we started to discuss and reshape the SBS Transit Rail way of doing things, to create a new set of processes and systems that could completely transform the mindset and willingness to do and sustain something that was probably going to be regarded as impossible.

There have been so many slogans in so many companies over the years, each aiming to capture a moment in time that 'it will be different and much better this time' that we were keen to avoid one. Most long term staff knew that these slogans generally lacked authenticity. We did however think it would be valuable to establish some principles which would act as a reference during discussions about priorities and targets.

The aim here was to document a set of principles which would be timeless but which, looking back, underpinned the periods in our careers when the various organisations we had been involved in had performed at their best and had exceeded all stakeholder expectations.

It seems as though Railway O&M Managers like to keep changing their organisational structures even though the key deliverables rarely change. A benefit of the Guiding Principles is their timelessness, that constant reference.

Career Observations

SBS Transit, Singapore

Elsewhere I highlight my 'aha' moment in 1985 in MacDonald's in Heidelberg Germany when their disciplined application of their processes and systems ensured the product tasted and presented exactly the same as it would in any other city or country. Their standard, proven processes and systems, no constant change as managers changed, no flavor of the month changes – just precision and discipline.

The creating of this standard discipline, coupled with the Guiding Principles redefined the DNA in SBS Transit's culture. That these are reportedly still in place, as is the hierarchy of review meeting structure, unchanged after six years has, in my opinion, enabled SBS Transit to be able to predict outcomes across all aspects of their business. A system. They are managing a system. Just like MacDonald's.

- False and Unsupported Claims that Safety is our first priority

Examples of false claims regarding the boast that 'safety is our top priority' are found in each of the six O&M Organisations reviewed between 2017 and 2020
    - Investigations with no corrective action plans
    - Poor reliability with no improvement plans

- Rules and Operating Procedures and Work Instructions which have not ben reviewed, validated, monitored or complied with for many years.
- Operating staff with no Competence Assurance Plans in place
- Emergency Management Plans where there are inadequate staff numbers and untrained people to implement them if called upon to do so.
- A refusal for Boards and/or CEOs to commit to provide the required resources to resolve issues in their Health and Safety Policies.

In Singapore, before launching out on what became our reliability revolution in 2015, I was conscious that newly appointed managers often open with a 'this is a new beginning', 'a new direction for everybody' to great acclaim forgetting that the long time employees have heard it all before and are unlikely to be freshly inspired, I documented my 'timeless truths', those 'truths' which had revealed themselves to guide, from my experience, the best organisational performance and alignment. What emerged was my Guiding Principles.

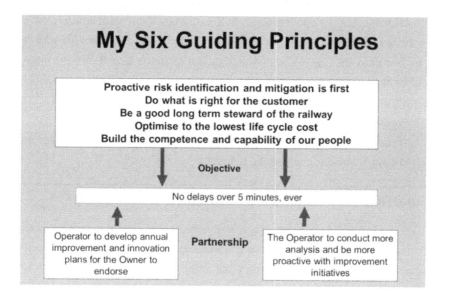

One: Safety is always first.

I don't really like this one, but I am keen to avoid controversy. Many organisations say that safety is their top priority without having much evidence to support it. It suggests that Safety is something discrete whereas I have come to see the proactive, systematic identification and mitigation of risk as much more useful since it can and should be a central philosophy applied to all areas of the business including safety, reliability, customer service, competency assurance, asset management etc.

The avoidance of loss of control, unexpected and unwanted events is the aim, to keep the organisational defences in a healthy state as articulated by James Reason.

Managers must act on precursor events. It is extremely unusual for loss of control events, delays or accidents, to be caused by a confluence of factors and weaknesses that are not well known. For example, at least of 38 of the 41 delays over 5 minutes in 2014 and 2015 on the North East Line were caused by well known vulnerabilities attests to this. In other Rail O&M organisations where I have provided assistance over the past decade or so, there were very few cases of delays where the causal factors were not widely known.

An analysis of the poor reliability of the commuter system in South London in 1986, In ScotRail in 1991, in Melbourne in 1994 and again in 2009 and in SBS Transit in 2015 were staring the organisation in the face, if only the management were looking, or knew how and where to look and how to see.

My alternative Principle would be as follows:

Proactive risk identification and mitigation of risk is always first

Throughout my career, the importance of being proactive has emerged as the critical behaviour in achieving success.

Two: Do what is right for the customer.

If you follow this Principle, particularly when there are choices not related to safety, it will rarely get you into trouble. It took SBS Transit to focus on reliability, the key driver of customer satisfaction and to face up to other key challenges impacting on passengers or the community (noise, escalators, handrails etc) to sustainably and systematically improve both an understanding of risks and challenges and performance in all aspects of the business

Since most Rail O&M organisations claim to put their customers. requirements close to first, it is shocking that the causal signs of poor reliability go untreated so often.

Three: Be a good long-term steward of the railway.

Most managers have relatively short shelf lives, and Boards often have even shorter financial targets, yet the decisions made by managers often have significant long term impacts.

The obligation that we accepted in SBS Transit Rail was that we would make decisions that benefited our successors, and theirs, that we would never deliberately make a decision to make their job harder. That meant we incurred costs to assist in that objective, not seeking short term reward.

The hard push to minimise costs in SMRT to maximise profitability between 2002 and 2009 came home to roost in 2010 when a series of major delays and breakdowns uncovered that not only had many of the critical asset and system conditions run down but worse, the senior management had conditioned their teams to make do, to minimise costs. This malaise was reflected by the deterioration in reliability over a decade on the East West and North South Lines but a sense of hopelessness in respect of the reliability of the Bukit Panjang LRT.

Perhaps the opening up of the 'two railway syndrome', the difference between the written Rules and Operating Procedures and Work Instructions and what the staff were actually doing emerged in this period too. The Judicial findings into the multiple staff fatalities at Pasir Ris in 2016 would suggest so.

This Principle is challenging for Boards and Senior Managers because it requires them not to adopt short term strategies but to create an organisational capability and culture to hand down to your successors, and theirs.

In Part seven, when considering the rights of the Owner and the obligations of the O&M Company the apparent conflict between the O&M Company and this Guiding Principle is considered recognising that the often private sector Company's Board's primary obligation is to their shareholders under the

Corporations Acts, not the long term stewardship or requirements of the Railway.

Four: Optimise to the lowest life cycle costs.

This follows on from being a good steward in that it recognises the need to ensure the best long term value for the railway. It forbids O&M managers from making short term savings which weaken the underlying capability of the organisation.

In all the various railway regimes, the Operator has control over costs: the allocation of resources whereas revenue is generally driven by others.

As with Guiding Principle regarding stewardship Part Seven also considers the apparent conflict between the Legal obligations of the O&M Company's Board and the long term life cycle costs. The private company is likely to put profit before the long term interests of the railway which leaves the Owner/State Authority as needing to ensure these Guiding Principles are protected within the commercial contracts. Experience with relatively short term franchises suggests that neither of Guiding Principles three or four are well protected.

Five: Build the competence and confidence of the people.

Frontline Staff

The mission delivers are the people who work in and support the O&M organisations.

To deliver and sustain the safest and highest performance requires capable, aligned, competent and confident staff.

As with safety, I have found that most senior O&M managers pay lip service to this, particularly for Managers and Supervisors.

The key weaknesses and lessons from the Inquiry into the Kings Cross Fire are frequently found to be evident in the late 2010s in many Rail O&M organisations.

Kings Cross Fire, November 1987
31 Deaths

- London Underground's Approach to Safety
  - Described as reactive
- Many of the shortcomings had been identified before
  - Internal Inquiries had not been considered adequately or acted upon. Lessons which junior management had considered should be learned were not followed up by senior management.
- Staffing
  - The staff on duty were not in a state of high readiness to act in case of an emergency.
  - There were inadequate numbers on duty to implement required controls in an emergency
- Equipment
  - The staff forgot that there was a sprinkler system that could have put the fire out, but nobody was trained or authorised to use it.
- Combat Readiness
  - There is a need to establish a proper level of safety at each station which can be met by either people or equipment

The Kings Cross Fire revealed a lack of readiness in respect to having the necessary equipment and staff in place to implement the emergency management plan and ensuring that the staff were in a state of high readiness. Even though this tragic accident was a long time ago the lessons do not seem to be well known or to have informed the DNA of Rail O&M Managers about major risks and how they should be managed. Why does the industry seem unable to learn about these sort of things?

In reviews of five major Operators between 20015 and 2020 all fail to pass the Kings Cross Fire test. Where are the Rail Regulators? The obligation is for processes, equipment and people to be in a state of readiness.

A review of nine underground station Operators between 2011 and 2020 revealed that in at least six of them there is no ongoing assessment of the readiness of key staff in major stations including underground stations, or Control Room staff.

Who has failed? Boards, Senior Managers and Regulators yet they all say that safety is their first priority.

Managers and Supervisors

While technicians, train drivers all require specific skills and capabilities, usually with ongoing assessment and monitoring this is rare for managers.

Supervisors are the real standard setters. They determine what is acceptable in the 'field of play' so to speak, and are often talked about as being the experts, yet they are often untrained and therefore incompetent, as are their managers. It would seem that the risk exposure to individuals and organisations is not appreciated.

Later in the book attention is drawn to the widespread subconscious incompetence of most O&M Managers, incompetent in that they have never been trained to ensure that they can discharge their responsibilities properly. It wouldn't happen for technical or key operations staff such a train drivers or control room staff. The Authorities would not allow it.

Whose fault is it that this incompetence is common? The accepted culture of what is normal, the reliance to follow previous leaders' examples. The blind leading the blind. Scary really.

Six: Partnership

Singapore's 1996 White Paper 'A World Class Land Transport System' recognises that the quality of the Land Transport System is a critical enabler of the social and economic efficiency of the Island State'. "It helps to maintain Singapore's competitive edge'. The same applies to many wealthy first world cities such as London, Paris, New York and Sydney. The respective road networks are unable to do the heavy lifting into and from major centers. It is their value rather than their cost that has guided the policy makers who approved the building of the rail capacities.

As critical shapers of the social and economic efficiency of many cities it is essential and often the case that partnerships between various Government Agencies and Rail O&M Operators are properly integrated.

There is however another powerful dimension of partnership which is often overlooked or not widely appreciated. That is the partnership that exists between different levels of O&M Organisations and between their departments.

I came to see Partnership in two perspectives
- Between major external parties
- The internal interdependencies within organisations, not only between Departments but more importantly between the senior management and their teams, usually at 5 levels.

For Internal Partnerships, I observed

My Apprenticeship Years

Supervisors in Ipswich, Victoria Station and Swansea who had many frustrations and incredible insights on how some long term seemingly intractable problems could be fixed.

As a young manager I used to take their frustrations and insights and try to resolve them. There were three incredible outcomes.

- They were absolutely delighted that 'at last, a manager was going to help'.
- That I learned so much about the problems in the nitty gritty which I would not otherwise have learned about.
- A mood of optimism that things were on the up, that everything was possible emerged. What great days they were. So many wonderful memories of those lifers.

In Melbourne between 1994 and 1997 I made it my habit to take three train cab rides per week. I always asked the drivers the same question. If I could do something that would make it easier for you to do a good job what would it be.

I used to write down their issue and follow it up. The same day I would drop a note to say that I would follow up their issue and get back to them, which I always did.

The manager's job is to help resolve frustrations.

The rewards are great

- From Chris Daughton at Victoria I learned the power of the follow up note to front line staff and supervisors.
- They have many frustrations and ideas which they would like somebody to be interested in. They want to help too.
- In several jobs I was issuing follow up notes everyday to acknowledge what they had told me then after the issue had been followed up, usually resolved.
- It wasn't hard but it helped to create one team. They knew I cared and that I was interested. More powerful than glossy brochures and videos

Simon.

Thank you for your informative letter of 5 /" /97 pertaining to Cpmeng train hand operated pilot valves.
I always felt the spring tolerance tension was unreasonable.
I appreciate you listening to my concerns and taking the issue up.
I realise you are a busy man.
Best Wishes — Kel Cox Frankston.

It helped to resolve lots of relatively minor issues but there were three longstanding benefits:

- They knew that I was interested.
- Most of their suggestions and issues were resolved, sometimes requiring money to be re-allocated, sometimes a work practice change.
- The performance improved a lot, and a great deal of the industrial relations 'noise' went away.

I never realised its impact until 13 years after I had left Melbourne and took up an interim management role with MTM in 2010.

I took a cab ride during an evening peak. The driver remembered me from before and had guessed my probable destination.

Fifteen minutes later, about five minutes before I was going to get off, out of the blue he said, 'I have an answer to your question'. I hadn't asked him a question, so he reminded me of my old practice from the 90s.

He had an important to him safety issue which worried him, and he asked if I could follow it up for him. 'Amazing', after 13 years. The issue was resolved for him, and the others.

Building a partnership is essential and not so hard.

My Senior Leadership Years

For the Sydney Olympic Rail Task there was requirement to achieve a utilisation of 98% of the Rolling Stock every day, all day became evident as the detailed resource requirements emerged. There could be no more trains, it was too late for that.

We told the Rolling Stock team what the requirement was and asked them to do three things:

- Go and develop a plan of how you are going to do it.
- Come and tell us what resources you required.
- Come back and tell us what decisions you needed from us to enable you to get there.

No external consultants, just using their own insights and experience.

Within a few months they had devised a plan, having declared that it was just impossible, they had a list of risks and challenges which would need to be managed and over a few more months came up with a very detailed plan which they subsequently delivered.

The senior management team used to review, test and verify their plans using our experience and insights to enable them and to give them confidence and encouragement. Their collective pride in the Plan's delivery was immense. What champions!

I consequently came to understand

This management thing isn't so hard. The lifers have incredible insights and frustrations which they want managers to resolve. You don't have to be the expert yourself. I learnt in those Ipswich, Victoria, Swansea and Melbourne days that I could trust the supervisors and frontline and that I could help them. I needed them and as their imposed facilitator they needed us too and together we could do some great things.

From this I learned about internal partnerships, their power and cultural impact too.

I also learned that you ignore these people's insights at your peril, certainly if you want them to bring their brains to work. Who doesn't want to feel as though they can contribute to improved performance and less frustration? Hardly anybody in my experience.

Internal Partnerships

Front line supervisors are a great source of knowledge when it comes to identifying frustrations that prevent the system working properly. They don't always have the answer, but they do know what doesn't work – they live with it every day.

The various levels of supervisors and managers bring different experiences and expertise to the task. Giving them the chance to be involved in the development and verification of improvement initiatives aligns the whole team, shows respect and acknowledges the different perspectives that they bring and builds a powerful momentum to move forward.

They are also best placed to communicate with and align the front-line staff.

<u>A Success Case Study</u>

In SBS Transit Rail between 2015 and 2017, when the Engineering Departmental Heads had to develop and document their Asset Management Plans, in line with their universal obligations they had no choice but to delve into their organisation to ensure that asset performance and condition at sub system and critical component level was properly understood and that their risks and challenges and proposed mitigation measures were aligned and likely to improve reliability, condition and reduce the associated risks. The senior managers could not do that on their own.

What emerged were deeply shared analysis and mitigation plans at several organisational levels.

When the Operations team were challenged to improve their decision-making and precision of intervention to reduce the length of any delays after asset failures they had to involve and take notice of different levels of people with their various ideas and insights.

The staff turned their brains on. They worked together in their Departmental teams and between Departments. It was wonderful to see the energy, ownership and ambition emerge.

By contrast, a traditional, heavy handed, 'I know best' approach from senior managers turns the brains off and reduces ownership, enthusiasm, and results. **The staff at all levels become compliers only.**

<u>A Failure Case Study</u>

A major Train Operator reviewed between 2017 and 2020 was suffering from very poor performance. The supervising Government Agency had requested, received and rejected the Operator's Improvement Plan as 'missing any valid analysis and credibility'.

A third-party review revealed that the senior supervisors and experienced operational planners all agreed with each other that a certain pathway should be followed to significantly resolve the various challenges.

The senior management team of the Business on receiving the analysis and advice rejected it since they had already decided between themselves what action should be taken.

Not only were the senior staff disappointed for themselves, but they felt completely detached from and disillusioned with their senior managers.

Over a three-year period that organisation has maintained its position as an underperforming, unreliable peak hour rail Operator. The risks and challenges were severe, the analysis was conducted, and a plan developed. The senior management decided they knew better. The experiences senior staff turned their brains off. At what cost?

This type of senior management behaviour has a big impact on the culture, the mood, the commitment, and the sense of pride at a critical interface between the mission creators and the mission deliverers.

External Partnerships

The relationship between the O&M Manager and the Operator with the Owner/Client is dealt with later under the relationship and responsibilities of Owners and Operators.

No Guiding Principle about profit

A highly successful UK based entrepreneur, when reviewing an early draft of this book was surprised that there was no reference to the affordability of the principles. In respect to the transformation of the reliability of the SBS Transit lines in Singapore he wanted to understand whether the strategy had been cost positive or negative, the impact on the bottom line.

Recognising the statement in Singapore's 1996 White Paper, A World Class Land Transport System where it stated that having a world class Land Transport System was a 'critical enabler of Singapore's social and economic efficiency', something which the Government invested in to enable, high performance outcomes including very limited car ownership, providing a best for railway' set of principles which fitted within the Government's philosophy.

In the short term in SBS Transit Rail there was an increase in costs, but those costs would have had to have been incurred in time as part of a reactive and disruptive culture. While this book does not put a value on the reduced impact of disruption to the passengers, community at large and the internal 'loss' associated with investigations, and short-term changes in priorities and resource allocation etc, the hidden costs of unexpected events including delays and accidents has been judged by others to be very high and lost in the normal business accounts.

The value to the community, in social and economic terms, of having a highly dependable, highly reliable railway to use is high but not quantified in this assessment. **The SBS Transit's North East Line went from having a delay over five minutes every three weeks to one per year.**

> When it comes to essential utilities, including water and electricity, I am of the view that they are societal value enablers rather than cost centers. Since it has become rare to suffer water or electricity outages why can't rail deliver the same level of certainty?

Did the approach which we undertook in SBS Transit cost money? Yes, but the value it provided in broad social and economic terms was significant. Greater than the costs? I don't know but we were able to persuade the Board that our approach would be good for business, so we pushed on.

Would a different approach where 21 delays over 5 minutes per year rather than one be endorsed under a budget saving initiative? I don't think so.

I came to understand that, as a consequence

When we were having discussions about how to handle a particular issue a reference back to the Guiding Principles proved to be useful.

Three broad reflections have occurred to me since 2015 when I first drafted these Guidelines which we reshaped and adopted in SBS Transit Rail.

As stewards of the railway, we became quite good at not taking only a short term perspective of challenges and risks when a tactical rather than a strategic response could have effectively kicked the issue down the road.

The power of the internal partnership and the recognition of the mutual on multiple levels within an organisation to be able to excel was important. Between the members of the senior management team we identified recurring themes when we shared our career highlights. There was no 'I' in team for a reason.

We also looked at challenges within a context of 5 to 10 years rather than within the existing budget cycle. The consequences of that was that we felt obliged to act once we had identified something that was not right.

When issues arose that previously might have been 'kicked down the road' we came to understand that such a behaviour was us failing to 'take all reasonable steps'. As such, the Guiding Principles and our legal obligations merged. Two important projects emerged that would not have done previously.

The new trains on the NEL trains had a circular handrail in the cars which were being bumped into by a couple of passengers per month according to the complaints feedback which meant that there were almost certainly many more. The handrails on the original trains had never been the source of complaints or injuries so we decided to refit the handrails at a cost of approximately S$1m. In many ways it was a test case for the adoption of the principles.

An analysis of injuries on escalators identified that the serious injuries from passengers falling were concentrated in the over 65 age group and concentrated further at Chinatown Station, much favored by older Singaporeans. This was a long standing, and well-known problem.

After a trial of trying to get old passengers to use the lifts failed, we sought an engineering solution. We discovered that shopping centers did not have a problem with old people falling and concluded that our escalators moving at 0.75m per second must be the primary cause since shopping centre escalators move at 0.5m per sec

A modification was developed and trialed to introduce dual speed escalators enabling 0.75m/sec in peak periods and 0.5 m/sec in off peak periods. **After deploying dual speed escalator control at Chinatown the falls and injuries vanished.**

The key to having to address these issues came from the Guiding Principles – proactively identify and mitigate risks and do what the customer wants you to do.

In 2017, the Land Transport Authority adopted the policy that all new escalators would be dual speed and that any escalators being upgraded at mid life had to be converted to dual speed. Not expensive but very proper from so many perspectives.

In 2016 a UK Safety Auditor visited SBS Transit Rail as part of a UK Pre franchise tendering qualification process. He commented that in the UK nobody would have expected us to act on the escalator or handrail issues saying that they probably wouldn't have passed the value for money assessment. Perhaps that is why the passenger rail reliability in so many cities is so poor? The managers are busy finding reasons not to act.

There is clearly a link between appetite, guiding principles and the creation of a culture which achieves much more than the sum of its parts. I will come back to this under Enabling Multiple Levels of Leadership within O&M Organisations later in Part One.

In Summary

The development of your own or a group Guidelines to establish signposts rather than moveable weather vanes will help to create some rules that always apply whatever the circumstances.

Once managers start justifying why they chose not to act, or only to act tactically, effectively 'kicking the can down the road' the rot sets in.

All my career highlights came when we collectively decided to make as perfect a job of things as we possibly could, as quickly as we could in line with our universal obligations, driven by the Health and Safety legislation. More of this in Section Two.

The move away from the normal safety or the customer grablines are our top priority claims helped to introduce a more nuanced, balanced and sustainable approach. The 'when in doubt do whatever the customer wants you to do' is a strong principle, not a grabline, as is the recognition that most managers are stewards of a long term challenge so should leave things better than they found it, often for the successor or their successor to enjoy the gains as we all strive to 'stand on the shoulders of giants' to take Isaac Newton's saying to a logical extent.

The emphasis that all the outcomes reflect the three critical success factors, the capability, capacity and alignment of the people is obvious but it properly reflects them as enablers of greatness if the senior management put in place arrangements to improve the three critical success factors.

If I was starting again, I would adopt this approach.

Create strong internal and external partnerships

Adopt a set of 'timeless truths', Guiding Principles. Adopt or modify mine if you wish but we all need signposts rather than weather vanes.

CHAPTER THREE

Qualified Experienced Senior Mangers

I came to believe that unless the senior management team members had the required skills and experience to provide professional and technical leadership, combined with the personal attributes to deliver the required objectives in a three to five year timeframe the likelihood of achieving sustained high performance was very limited.

It continues to amaze me how often senior managers are appointed who lack the required qualifications, experience and skills to deliver the required deliverables. It allows the thinking that the challenges are somehow too insurmountable to achieve traction.

It is the task of senior managers to find a way, and to take their people on the journey. As this book highlights there are some standout examples of where 'the impossible' has been delivered and where poor performance has become institutionalised.

While appetite for excellence is key the capability, skill and experience of senior managers is also critical.

Career Observations

The frequent lack of recognition of the Legal and Technical Accountabilities of Senior Managers which are derived from the Health and Safety at Work legislation and include the following:

- Leading the resolution of complex technical challenges, particularly across asset interfaces. If not them then who?
- Establishing and approving selection and competency standards, for staff and contractors and ensuring that they are met and maintained.
- Establishing safe methods of work and ensuring that they are monitored and complied with.
- Establishing and approving Procedures and Work Instructions.
- Establishing and approving technical standards.
- Ensuring that unplanned and unexpected events are investigated and follow-up actions implemented to minimise the likelihood of recurrence.

The lack of recognition for post holders to meet minimum qualifications, skills and experience of Senior Managers.

There are now many senior managers and Departmental Heads in O&M roles in Singapore and Australia where the minimum experience, skills and qualifications requirement in UK legislation and HSE Guidelines are not met, and many cases where there are no minimum qualifications and experience criteria for the selection of senior managers.

A tendency to say that a person is a good candidates and make an appointment without any reference to a minimum criteria is common.

The apparent lack of appreciation for highly experienced, highly qualified senior managers who were able to provide high value in terms of technical and professional leadership.

As a test, look at the high and low performing organisations and look at the qualification and experience profiles of their Senior Managers. I think the results reflects the skills and experience profiles of the senior teams. There seems to be many examples of the wrong candidate being appointed.

A need for prior Rail experience? No

For many senior roles the qualifications, skills and experience are held be people outside the rail industry, particularly where safety, the use and maintenance of sophisticated equipment and systems, reliance on precise procedures and disciplined application of knowledge is required. The need is for relevant experience.

Those that come from outside the industry enrich the industry's DNA, reducing the insularity and relatively closed access to talent. In the UK there are many examples of high-quality managers coming from both the mining industry and the armed services.

In Singapore, Jeffrey Sim, when he joined SBS Transit Rail as head of Rolling Stock for the North East Line in 2015 brought expertise, energy and a mindset that significantly enhanced the broader O&M team which he now leads (2022) as the Rail CEO.

Similarly, the increased number of women in senior positions have also enabled the cultural mix to become richer and more reflective of the talents available in society at large.

The appointment of the wrong candidate for the course. Senior Managers

The appointment of managers and supervisors is probably the most important task that Rail Managers have – the consequences, both intended and unintended are long lasting.

Before embarking on the selection and appointment process experience shows that the early identification of the tasks and deliverables that the successful candidate will be expected to deliver increases the likelihood that a suitable candidate will be appointed who has the proven skills, experience and attributes to be successful.

How should managers get that experience? By working at different levels, ideally in different places so as not to think that there is only one way, by reading and studying around the subject, by asking lots of questions so that you leave interactions more knowledgeable and by doing lots of 'go-look-see' on location visits, to get a fuller understanding of the challenges and frustrations which front line staff and supervisors are faced with on a regular basis.

It is up to individuals to qualify and skill themselves up to win the right to sit at a bigger table.

A status quo Leader when a big change person was required resulting in organisational and individual failure which is very sad to see.

A 'big change' leader for a big challenge where, along with the appropriate qualifications and experience is able to take the organisation and its culture to a new sense of high performance.

I came to understand that, as a consequence

The performance reflects the expertise of the senior team

Relatively inexperienced senior managers who lack either or both sufficient relevant qualifications or experience so are unable to provide either technical or professional leadership outside normal General Management skills. So, who is in charge? Who is accountable? Surely to be held accountable the person must have the skills, experience and qualifications to do so?

I read this which guided my thinking and practice

Ensuring Safety in Britain's Railways 1993

It emphasised the need to ensure that only sufficiently qualified, skilled and experienced people should be allowed to hold the key posts to ensure that the Organisations had the proven capability to discharge their accountabilities.

It also emphasised the need for Organisations, and key post holders, to be willing and capable.

The UK's Railway Safety Case Regulations, 1996:

They make specific reference to "Staff who are critical to safety, including drivers and signalmen will he certificated by a body approved by the Executive, to standards approved by the Executive."" but are not definitive about managers.

Not having any form of required accreditation for O&M managers appears to be an omission that has not served the industry well, not specifically in the UK but more generally.

By contrast, in Jim Collin's Good to Great he asserts that an organisation needs the best people in the country to build a great company misplaces, in my opinion, the essential ingredient of getting more from the sum of the parts as I experienced in Melbourne and Sydney between 1994 and 2000 and later in Singapore.

Certainly, in each of those three examples I don't think other industry players would have regarded any of the senior team as being 'best in the country' in our fields even though the outcomes were.

If I was starting again, I would adopt this approach.

Two key issues stand out for me.

Firstly, my first step before embarking on a recruitment process would be to identify the key tasks and essential deliverables for the next three years, including the level of outcomes required before secondly, identifying the ideal skills and experience profile which would make it likely that thirdly the candidate will be able to be successful in delivering what is required.

Only at that point would I start the process of fourthly, finding suitable candidates, those that fitted the desired profile.

This might seem very logical but in practice it appears the four steps are not undertaken with many examples of appointing people who 'we think is a good person' without any basis or examination which results mostly in disappointment for the selected person and the Business.

Secondly, having appointed managers to handle a particular set of challenges and risks it seems logical that once the 'period of office', the challenge delivery period, has passed and a new set of risks and challenges has been identified the suitability of the person to the role should be revisited with removal being an option involving redeployment or departure – back to horses for courses – to avoid organisational constipation with the wrong person in the wrong seat on the bus. The objective is to create and maintain a dynamic, stimulating culture.

After the successful delivery of the Olympic Rail Task in Sydney in 2000 I supported the Government's desire to seek a new style of leader for a quite different set of challenges. It was good for me and the State Rail Authority where I had been the CEO for the previous 1000 days.

CHAPTER FOUR

Business Rhythm of PDSA and Planning

I came to believe that unless an O&M Organisation has a well-structured Plan, Do, Study, Act (PDSA) process across all aspects on the O&M
challenge, looking at day to day, weekly, monthly and annual to five
year timeframes of risks, challenges and opportunities within an integrated
hierarchical framework it is not possible to create and sustain high performance outcomes in all aspects of the O&M Business.

More than anything, organisations are defined by their processes and systems. Along with analysis, investigations, understanding, risk identification
and mitigation these processes and systems underpin the extent to which the
organisation is personality or process and system driven.

High performing O&M Organisations are not personality dependent and
have well established processes and systems. I first came to understand this
while sitting in a MacDonald's in Heidelberg in Germany in 1985 when I found
the food looked and tasted the same as it did in London – sure sign of a ma-
ture, disciplined organisation.

This is what we tried to put in place in Singapore between 2015 and 2018
as we tried to create a set of processes and systems that would enable a delay
free railway.

With a very high commitment to the Universal Obligations of O&M management within and between each Department and across the Business we

were able to move from reporting on historical performance and hoping about the future to a well-informed, confident regime of predictive regime.

This confidence came from a disciplined look back and looking forward hierarchy of structured meetings. Within a 12 week cycle all aspects of performance and risk were looked at in detail looking up to 10 years ahead. The avoidance of loss of control events meant no more surprises. If we had a loss of control event it meant that the management had missed something, it had failed.

This 'Business Rhythm' is so called because it reflects the frequent and integrated series of review meetings which enable participants to have structured 'touch points' enabling every aspect of performance, every risks and challenge to be considered in a systematic process.

High performing O&M requires managers to keep many 'balls in the air' so as to be able to understand and assess the risks, adjusting priorities and resources as required in an informed proactive manner, to minimise the likelihood of an unexpected, unwanted, loss of control event.

These series of review meetings are a key part of a management system. There is a predictable rhythm to it. Not having this is likely to lead to a culture dominated by either an acceptance or a reactive approach to avoidable loss of control. Nobody wants that. It is both very expensive in terms of time and is very disruptive.

Career Observations

Ineffective meetings requiring no preparation or strategy

Unfortunately, it is common for most meetings to become absorbed by matters arising where previously discussed issues are discussed again and where the focus is trapped on the recent past rather than the future – very boring to sit through.

An effective use of meetings

I was introduced to the disciplined concept of PDSA by my Rolling Stock colleagues in ScotRail in 1991 and had a moment of self realisation that without a structured set of interlinking meetings we were going to be busy but unfocussed and probably not get anywhere which seems to be a common feature in most organisations.

The creation of a set of meetings on reliability, safety, investigations and finance led in time not only to great progress by the team but also a mechanism in which there was a structure in which to consider all important matters of the Business.

Until this time, like most railway managers, the main focus had concentrated on dealing with active failures which are due to individual error rather than the underlying systemic problems – the PDSA process revealed those and challenged us not to sweep them under the carpet.

A cultural improvement opportunity

Herein sits another lesson. Senior Managers are like actors on a stage under the spotlight, being observed all the time by subordinates. If the leader sweeps the challenges under the carpet everybody sees it and knows. By contrast, the opposite is also true.

After only a few year of working it had become apparent that almost everybody who goes to work wants to do a very good job and be part of a great and successful mission. It is the managers' job to shape and enable it to happen, to let as many people as possible enjoy satisfaction and success in their work. Unfortunately, for reasons unknown to me, most managers are Process Administrators rather than shapers of possibilities, leaders.

A well-structured, disciplined Business Rhythm provides a mechanism for Organisations to be stable and predictable results. This relies on the consequential understanding of performance, risks and challenges and resourced mitigation plans. The meetings are useful for monitoring, creating a shared understanding of performance, risks and challenges and the mitigation plans. They are useful for adjusting priorities and plans but also for encouraging and empowering analysis and curiosity while acting as great forums for celebrating individual and team success.

The discipline becomes infectious as does the sense of achievement and pride. Certainly, in Melbourne in the 1990s, Sydney for the Olympics, the startup of the North East Line and the Sengkang-Punggol LRT in 2003 in Singapore and the SBS Transit reliability transformation after 2015, that was the case.

A Case Study: SBS Transit 2015 to 2017 and beyond

The Business Rhythm provided a framework in which to look at data in a systematic way from which we learned so much. Firstly, we quickly came to acknowledge that we only had a very limited understanding of the patterns of failures, delay and late running which prevented us from knowing how and when to intervene to improve performance.

The interesting bit was that this same subconscious incompetence, group think or 'learned helplessness' that had been apparent in the then Southern Region in the mid-1980s as a Duty Manager at Victoria Station was also apparent in Melbourne in 1994 and in Singapore in 2015. What is it about the industry that allows this Learned Helplessness or incompetence to prevail? Keep reading as to gain an understanding and insight into this journey of discovery.

What is interesting about this journey was the need to abandon strongly held but incorrect assertions about what was systematically going wrong. These assertions needed to be unlearned at the beginning of the various improvement journeys. The key to the success in Melbourne in the 1990s was the willingness of the senior management team to try new ways of working. They were most definitely willing, if not quite able due to a lack of exposure and training.

There is a benefit of having many systematic touch points enabling short, medium and long term objectives and critical deliverables to be knitted into a single dialogue.

I came to understand that, as a consequence

The Business Rhythm was the glue which enabled the management teams in Melbourne, Sydney and Singapore to achieve a level of excellence that, in each case, exceeded the stakeholders' expectations and enabled the mission to not only be delivered but celebrated. In each case, while the results were outstanding it was the understanding of how the risks and challenges were identified and managed that gave the most satisfaction. In each case the outcomes were not a fluke.

Good meetings are focused work to enhance understanding, adjust resource allocations and refine focus – stimulating to participate in.

The adoption of a structured Plan, Do, Study, Act across Safety and Reliability review mechanism provided a vehicle for both individual and collective learning.

Without this simple discipline the teams I worked with would probably not have enjoyed their subsequent success. The teams learned to question long standing assumptions about how we worked, how we prioritized and what our individual responsibilities were to avoid unplanned, unexpected events, accidents or delays particularly.

Without an effective framework, a Business Rhythm which covered all areas of risk in the O&M circle, crisis keep on emerging, distracting everybody and resulting in a culture which reacts and only responds to short term problems

It was possible to tie all the business risk and opportunity issues into a seamless, flexible, dynamic with multiple levels of ownership

That a strong Governance framework enabled high levels of ownership, innovation along with multiple levels of leadership where brains were turned on at the gate.

It provided that MacDonald's like discipline, processes and systems that underpinned the shift to such high levels of predictability and confidence regarding risk control and performance.

I later read this which reinforced my thinking and practice

Meetings, bloody meetings: John Cleese

This video uses humour to highlight the absurd approach that typify many meetings and what needs to be done to avoid the normal pitfalls. Similarly, Cleese's video on 'the dreaded performance review' make compelling viewing.

Jim Collins' Good to Great

The research of the successful companies studied highlighted the importance the need for disciplined people, disciplined thinking and disciplined action.

Well-structured meetings help with this. They are essential in helping to bring the Universal Obligations of O&M Managers to life. More of this in Part Two.

- To improve organisational understanding of performance and conditions.
- To understand and test the identification of risks.
- To test the robustness and resource requirements for the risk mitigation plans.
- To monitor and celebrate achievements.

The other key point of discovery that resonated with me was the description of what Collins called the flywheel effect.

As Collins wrote (P165) 'the flywheel image captures the overall feeling within the organisations under transformation. There was no single defining action, no grand programme, no one killer innovation, no solitary luck break, no wrenching revolution. It came about through a cumulative process, step by step, action by action that led to a 'take-off point' resulting in sustained and spectacular results'.

By 1994 when I moved to Melbourne, I already had a sense from Swansea and Scotland days that long serving staff, particularly managers and supervisors were cynical when new bosses turned up proclaiming that everything would be different and much better than before. They were, though, open to participating in a journey of collective discovery and learning if they thought the intent was well considered and respected their insights and experience.

In Melbourne in 1994 and in SBS Transit Rail in 2015 there were no big announcements or launches of a 'Transformation Programme'. In both cases the organisation embarked on an understated journey in which systems and processes were developed building a quiet confidence, repeatedly working on the right things before the 'flywheel affect' kicked in in 1996 in Melbourne and in 2017 in Singapore, where reliability improved, appearing to suddenly 'take-off' rising to a level that had been perceived as impossible only two years earlier.

In both cases the multi layered Governance Structure of meetings were where the mission got formed and brought to life. Meetings were where the work was done, decisions made, and progress monitored and success cele-brated. In SBS Transit Rail we ate a lot of chocolate cakes!

Slowly, the mindset of what was possible changed and established a new shared determination to deliver something that had been regarded as impos-sible. It came from a gradual, systematic, disciplined but non-stop process. In both Melbourne and Singapore performance continued to improve for a fur-ther four years after my moving on.

If I was starting again, I would adopt this approach.

The multi-faceted hierarchy of meetings in SBS Transit Rail was the most comprehensive set of meetings I used in my career. The confidence that emerged as we regularly touched all bases, reviewed all risks, existing and emerging, making adjustments to priorities on the way, became very power-ful.

My understanding in December 2021 is that the structure and discipline is still in place. The organisational processes and management systems are strong. Another feature of SBS Transit Rail is that the organisational structure has hardly changed in 20 years with adjustments only at the margin as some new challenges have emerged.

Some observers of the SBS Transit Rail meeting structure said they thought that we had too many meetings. Out of an 8-weekly cycle of 320 hours, 40 8-hour days, the Business Rhythm took up about 20% of the senior team's time. It was definitely not a case of 'you have too many meetings' as some outside our bubble told us. Our collective understanding of our risk pro-file in many key aspects of the business was high. In every area the outcome moved from being Administrative and acceptable to High Performance.

If I was starting again, I would adopt the framework we used in SBS Transit Rail in 205/2016.

One more thing. Many O&M organisations are in a continuous restructur-ing mode. How can one embed strong management processes and systems in such an environment, particularly when the fundamental risks and chal-lenges remain largely unchanged over the decades? When in doubt, restruc-ture – it's treated as a substitute for dealing with the risks and challenges.

When I was at my best: Governance Structure Case Study

My second spell with SBS Transit was my final full time position in which I tried to bring together all the learning from my career in an attempt to reset the underlying culture and establish a management mechanism that enabled the whole organisation to excel. This case study reflects what was put in place.

SBS Transit Rail operate 3 Lines. They have responsibility for two driverless, fully automated Metro Lines, the North East Line and the Downtown Line, and the driverless, fully automated Sengkang-Punggol Light Rail System.

We established a very focused hierarchy of review meetings to help us understand performance, risks and the status of mitigation measures across various aspects of our business including safety, reliability, customer feedback, competence etc over several timeframes from one week to five years.

There were plenty of touch, test and review points. The structure and focus of these meetings is outlined below as a Good Practice example.

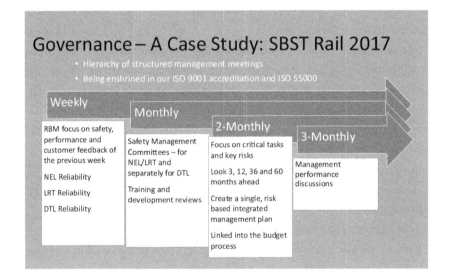

Reliability: Fault and Delay (F&D) meetings: 90 minutes

Each of the three Lines met separately, three times per week.
Led by Heads of Engineering and Operations for each Line.
Engineering and Operations Departmental Heads attended
No deputies or support staff were allowed.

- It was seen as essential that the Heads could provide their analysis and insights.
- They had to resolve interface challenges with their senior colleagues.
- They all had to be prepared which meant they had to have their own departmental reviews as part of their preparation.

This senior involvement was important in two respects.

- It brought the most experienced brains, and the most responsible to the room.
- It clarified the sense of importance of reliability matters.

Outcomes

- Many of the ongoing problems that were frequently occurring and causing difficulties to the daily operations were quickly resolved enabling concentration on resolving more serios but known challenges.

The Focus of these meetings

- The last 48 hours
- Status of investigations
- The next 48 hours

I came to understand, as a consequence:

These meetings had been going since 2003 but a habit had set in where previously attendance had been delegated to junior staff and the meetings had no authority and did not resolve complex, multi-departmental issues. They typified the Administrative culture of the day.

Almost immediately after the senior Heads attended, and the frequency went from twice to three times per week, many issues were quickly resolved leaving time to focus on more challenging issues.

Very soon afterwards, as system stability improved, reliability shifted upwards.

This absence of senior management from F&D meetings has been found in other Rail O&M organisations, As soon as the Senior Managers re-engaged reliability improved as it did in SBS Transit. This improvement was free!

A key success factor sits with the Chair. No speculative discussions, no filibustering. The meeting is work.

Weekly Business Review: Tuesday 0830 for 90 mins

Attendance (7)
- Business Head chaired the meeting
- Attendees included the head of safety, the heads of engineering and operations from the two lines and corporate HR.

Agenda: The meeting's purpose was to look at five matters only:
- The previous week
  - Safety and Security
    - All safety and security reports were noted.
    - Any late Safety Management Actions were raised.
    - All Safety Management Actions with deadlines within two weeks were noted.
  - Customer Feedback on each line
    - The purpose was to highlight opportunities of learning rather than the routine for feedback into our planning sessions.
  - Operational Overview
    - Only high level reporting
  - HR issues
    - More general management type issues.
    - Often the main discussion part of the meeting.
  - Key events for the following week
  - AOB

I came to understand, as a consequence:

One of the promises that the senior team made to each other was that we would be prepared on the relevant matters and that agreed management actions would always be completed on time.

We only looked at matters arising that had not been resolved quarterly on an exception basis. We did not waste our time by checking and discussing repeatedly the same matters.

From these meetings emerged the several initiatives including the following:

- A major redesign and improvement of the concrete plinths on the LRT structure which had opened up resulting on wheel banging noises.
- Modification to the hand rails on the new NEL trains which had caused tall people to knock their heads.
- The need to address old passengers falling on escalators.

<u>Weekly: Line Reliability:</u>

Structure
- Three Meetings
    - DTL Monday 1600 for 90 mins
    - NEL Tuesday 1400 for 90 mins
    - SPLRT Tuesday 1600 for 90 mins

Attendance
- Chaired by the Business Head
- Heads and Engineering and Operations for that line
- Heads of OCC and Engineering Departments for that line

Agenda
- Head of Traffic (OCC) gave a presentation on the previous week.
    - Provided the team with an opportunity to brief the Business Head on outcomes from the F&D meetings
- Monthly Update by two nominated Heads of Department in rotation
    - Update on Performance Improvement Plans
- Next 8 weeks
    - Critical deliverables
    - Emerging risks

I came to understand, as a consequence:

The Business Head was across the detail, the risks and the mitigation plans and was able to test of the thoroughness of the investigations and follow up from the F&D meetings.

While there was some professional tension where nobody wanted to be found wanting we were able to share and bounce ideas off each other.

The sharing of properly structured applied statistical analysis of sub system performance, along with emerging risks and mitigation plans transformed the language, narrative, transparency and the sense of possibility.

Focus improved and the recognition of Departmental inter dependence on behalf of the whole was realised. This collaboration emerged through the F&D and Weekly Review process. What fun we had.

In time, the level of confidence and evident capability became apparent. The paradigm that it was possible to avoid all unplanned, unexpected events grew at individual, Departmental and Business level emerged.

The bringing to life of the first Guiding Principle in respect of risk and the sixth Guiding Principle of enhancing the capability and confidence of our people were brought to life here.

Monthly: Safety Review – one meeting for each Line, each month: 90 minutes

Structure
- One meeting for NEL &SPLRT and a second for DTL

Attendance (12 – too many really)
- Chaired by the Business Head.
- Head of Safety and Heads of Engineering and Operations for that line
- All Operations and Engineering departmental Heads attended. No deputies allowed.

Agenda

- Status of safety management actions
  - Our first priority so don't miss the agreed date.
- Status of Audit and External review findings. Again, do not be late.
- Recent incidents
  - Passenger
  - Staff
  - Contractor
- Outcomes from investigations
- Upcoming exercises
- Presentation of a non-Singaporean accident investigation, not necessarily Rail related event by a Department Head, on rota-

I came to understand, as a consequence:

The mantra of not ever being late for an agreed safety management action was good.

The meeting was initially too passive with the Safety Team reporting on performance and status of action.

The introduction of the rotating presentation of external investigations brought out some fantastic learning opportunities. It also gave the Heads a chance to show intelligence and initiative which helped to raise the calibre of the discussion away from tactical, short term focus.

From these meetings we embarked on some key initiatives around:

- Acceptance that any injury or accident represented a failure of us as a team same as we came to regard a delay over 5 minutes.
- High risk escalators
- The transparency of the competence of Contractors staff
- OCC staff readiness to handle smoke alarms from a report from Washington DC
- Handholds on the new NEL trains
- The Guiding Principles of Safety first helped us not to push some of these longer-term issues under the carpet, as is often the case. A culture of action rather than complacency.

Monthly: Training – two meetings per month. Tuesdays at 1000: 90 minutes

Structure
- Meeting One: Operational
  - Selection, Training and Assessment status
  - Competency Assurance review
- Meeting Two: Management/Supervisor Development
  - Strengthening Organisational Capability

Attendance (7)
- Chaired by the Business Head
- Head of Rail HR
- Head of Rail Training attended the Operational meeting, with Head of Learning and Development of SBS Transit Corporate attended the Management meeting
- Heads of Engineering and Operations for each Line attended.

Agenda
- Operational
  - Status of recruitment plans
  - Status of Initial Training plans
  - Status of Competence Assurance Plans
- Management
  - Status of non-technical Training Plans
  - Government and Corporate Programmes
  - Three-year General Management skills and awareness priorities.

Benefits and Outcomes

This meeting enabled us to ensure that the recruitment and initial training programmes were delivered as designed, often with Departmental heads being required to release trainers to support the programme.

Same for Skills and Development. The short-term focus of middle managers can divert resources away from activities of medium and long term benefit without oversight.

It was the three-year outlook which emerged from the Quarterly Business Reviews that led us to putting in place proper data analysis and investigations courses.

It highlighted the need to do take 'best for railway' decisions on behalf of the successors, as required by our Guiding Principle three, 'to be a good long-term steward of the railway'.

This area consumes resources and can be regarded as non-essential in the short term. The day I left SBS Transit my CEO took 50% out of the following years budget for Supervisory and management training. Latent conditions emerge!

Quarterly: Thursday morning 0930 to 1230

Context

Except for the Training Meeting which is a mixture of operational and more strategic issues the Quarterly Review provided the context into which everything else fitted.

In the early period the meeting was held 8 weekly but moved out to quarterly after about 12 months as the granularity and control of the myriad of short term issues were pulled under tighter control.

As the programme and the team matured, we were able to start looking beyond the operational perspective and began to consider the risks and challenges facing the organisation over the next 3 to 5 years.

This look forward into the medium term had two main benefits:

- The highlighting of medium term capability issues
- Our more operational type plans which traditionally underpinned the budget cycle tended to enable medium to long term challenges away into the future since their resolution lies beyond the one year horizon.
- Two examples of issues that were brought to the fore by a three year look were the need to significantly strengthen the investigations and data analysis capability of the Line Managers.
- The other was the need to provide contemporary strategic management courses for the senior management team, and their successors.

Attendance (7)

- Facilitated by Business Head – not a prerequisite
- The head of Safety and Rail HR and the Heads of Engineering and Operations attended.

Agenda: Looking forward

- Next 6 weeks, 3, 6 and 12, 24 and 36+ months
  - What are the Critical deliverables in each time period?
  - What are the respective key risks and challenges?
  - Where do we need to adjust priorities/resource allocation?
- Beyond 24 and 36+ months
  - What are the medium to long term challenges or areas where we need to improve?
- Cascading the output
  - Thursday afternoon, on the same day
    - To Heads of Department for communications and validation.
      - This is the assessment of the senior team.
      - Do you think we have missed anything?
      - Do you endorse the assessment and the emerging plan?

I came to understand, as a consequence:

This process became the setter of the context and the medium-term roadmap into which everything else fitted.

It provided material for Department Heads to cascade to their people, not repeating it but tailoring it to the requirements and focus of their people. This is in line with their obligations under the Health and Safety Policy that the Departmental Heads specific obligations include the alignment and engagement of their people.

The decision to avoid big roadshows that have become the fashion in some places was deliberate. They tend to be preachy and do not give an opportunity for any real engagement. Sheep dipping in nature, where the farmer dips the whole flock to kill the lice, very much a one-way street – not communication.

Overall reflection

The Business Rhythm provided a firm context into which all our work fitted. We were aware of our performance, our risk profile looking at various timeslots from 3 weeks to 5 years along with our plans.

We had a joined up, integrated understanding of performance, risks, priorities and plans. As a team we managed the risks and challenges through our people. The internal processes and meeting structure provided that sense of no dependence on any individual. We were our processes and systems.

We were not running our Lines, the supervisors and front-line staff did that. We were managing it in a very disciplined, systematic way. Not only have the operational results been remarkable but the managers and staff seemed to like it too. Certainly, there was a strong sense of pride and confidence.

Out of an 8-weekly cycle of 320 hours, 40 8-hour days, the Business Rhythm took up about 20% of the senior team's time. It was definitely not a case of 'you have too many meetings' as some outside our bubble told us.

If I was starting again, I would adopt this approach.

Meetings should be as small as possible with all attendees having a stake in the discussions and decisions. No 'second rowers' to talk on behalf of the required manager. The required managers should know their stuff and be able to discuss it, having done their preparation beforehand if necessary.

In general, they should be focused and relatively short with 60 minutes being ideal but 90 minutes being the upper limit. There must have been a reason why University lectures were capped at 50 minutes. Presumably it is related to focused concentration times and the ability of keeping everybody on track.

Meeting should be tiered to provide review and a process of escalation and should cover all aspects of the Business.

The meeting structure should provide touch points for all parts of the business looking at the recent past, the short-term future and the medium to long term to provide both an operational focus and a strategic context.

CHAPTER FIVE

Building multi-level aligned leadership and ownership

*I*n my early years I found that the good supervisors and their staff were full of insights and ideas and were keen for help to resolve frustrations and to improve performance in almost all areas of the O&M challenge. These same people wanted the opportunity to help shape an exciting mission, to be proud to participate in its delivery.

From experienced supervisors and staff at London's Victoria station, to South Wales, ScotRail, Melbourne, Sydney and Singapore across 35 years becoming an enabling manager was easy. The staff had great insights, frustrations and ambitions if only they could be allowed to participate in the strategic and tactical thinking. It is the senior manager's job to enable them, and people at other levels, to bring their insights to the table and to respond to them.

This 'invisible people' factor was central to the planning and delivery of the Sydney Olympic Rail task, the start up of the North East line and Sengkang-Punngol LRT in Singapore and the reliability revolution in Singapore after 2015. The ownership, risk assessment and mitigation and accountability was multi layered.

Career observations

In my early career jobs, the seasoned supervisors ran the job. The Supervisors run the railway, they set the standards of what is acceptable and set the tone. In many ways they are the operational experts. They know what works, what doesn't work and have great insights to share.

The manager's job is to intervene when an opportunity to improve their systems presents itself, their approach.

The Servant Leader

At Victoria Station as a young Duty Manager in 1985 there was in no doubt that I was the servant leader to the experienced Senior Coordinators. To have acted otherwise would have led to a plethora of stories about my cock ups. To be a servant leader was less risky than being directive. It was a very good lesson.

In this context the manager does not have to be the expert. The role was to test and verify plans, to support the front-line staff and their supervisors, to provide the required resources, to monitor effectiveness, to provide feedback and to celebrate.

Being a servant leader has never been a problem. The role as a helper, an enabler and in recent years been more of a guide, a mentor and encourager providing significant opportunities to contribute something although some might say they ignored the guidance and advice at their own risk. Perhaps.

Swansea Area Manager 1988 -91

As Area Manager for South and West Wales with approximately 800 staff we had five business contracts:

- InterCity Great Western for who we provided about 30% of the train crew
- Local South Wales Train services to West Wales
- Three train load freight business contracts; Metals, Oil and a declining Coal business.

The passenger and freight business each had their own 24/7 coordinating centers a with each having their own supervisors in the field.

We established regular 'family gatherings' of the supervisor teams, usually on Saturdays at lunchtime with others acting in higher to relieve rostered supervisors so the whole 24/7 team could attend.

Their purpose was twofold: for us to get to know each other better, but more importantly to listen to their frustrations and to discuss our own perceptions of some emerging challenges.

We were all surprised at their value: the team building, the listening, the shared perspectives, the greater sense of purpose. What emerged was a whole list of things that we could all do to help each other and the team overall to improve our performance.

We were able to allow everybody a chance to shape the plan, to share and influence priorities and resource allocation. The response and emerging performance was remarkable as was the growing confidence of the supervisors as critical attitude and alignment influencers. We all rowed together.

The Olympic 2000 Rail Task

When helping to shape and oversee the development and delivery of the Olympic Rail Task in Sydney for the 2000 Olympics (the best ever according to the head of the IOC) there were four key work streams and multiple sub-elements within each of those.

Without a well-structured PDSA framework, our governance eco-system, it would have been impossible to keep abreast of the status of each, the key risks and challenges and the ability to adjust resource and priorities as required.

If the State Rail Authority had dealt with each work stream using established processes, the organisation would have been ready for the September 2000 opening ceremony in mid-2002. We had to change the way we did almost everything: selection and recruitment, training and assessment, timetable development, engineering work, construction of new infrastructure, major periodic maintenance of almost all assets.

The Cultural Impact in Sydney

The senior management was able to shape the required outcomes, but it was the multiple layers of ownership throughout almost all parts of the organisation where the expertise, knowledge and insights sat that provided the opportunity to create a complex web of interrelated plans to deliver the task.

It was a task which owed its success to many hundreds of people showing that they had all the leadership skills required – and that was before the days when people got sent on a course to become accredited leaders!

Creating Aligned Leadership at multiple levels of SBS Transit Rail.

As it was with the Olympic Rail Task, so it was with the SBS Transit Rail reliability improvement. In Sydney's case the mission was obvious which certainly contributed to the focus and shared determination to do whatever it takes, not that that had been sufficient in Atlanta in 1996.

In the SBS Transit case however the declared mission to reach an MKBF of 400k by 2018, a halving of the number of delays over five minutes compared to 2014 and 2015, the best years to date, there was not that shared understanding and buy-in.

That sense of the possible had to be created, a task that hung on the improved business processes and procedures.

Leong Yim Sing announced our new target in mid-December 2015 at an industry forum and then we had a terrible first quarter in 2016 but we had begun our journey. There was no way of turning back by then.

The possibility of success there was obvious. Of the previous 41 delays at least 38 were due to known factors so we needed to shift from a reactive to proactive mindset. It required a shift to more of a bottom-up than a top-down determination of risk identification and mitigation which typifies many rail organisations.

Of the previous 38 delays the senior engineers and their staff knew where the risks were and in most cases what mitigation measures would probably work best. This is normal but recognising it is, strangely, not.

The Senior Managers had to ask them to identify the critical risks and their proposed mitigation measures. The Management Review process tested the basis of their identified risk and the likelihood of the proposed measure being effective.

Once risk mitigation plans had been tested and verified the resources followed, very quickly almost every time releasing new energy and focus but also a sense of ownership.

The Management Review process tested the effectiveness of the new measures as they rolled out. A success rate of over 90% emerged, something I had experienced in previous jobs.

As with experience in Swansea and Sydney we could trust almost everybody to act in the company's interests all the time. Not to do so restricts the overall capability and commitment of 'experts' who, in my experience always want to help, to shape and deliver the mission.

Learning to build the multi-level commitment and ownership.

Over the previous 25 years since 1985 at Victoria Station it had been apparent that the long serving supervisors were very familiar with systemic problems. They were the source of enormous frustration. As a relatively inexperienced manager with almost no direct knowledge to teach them, another approach emerged which has lasted all these years.

ISO 55001, Asset Management, also helped to create the same multi level understanding, ownership and commitment. The Standard requires Asset Managers to be able to demonstrate key requirements:

- An understanding of asset performance and condition
- The identification of emerging risks
- Resourced risk mitigation plans.

Combined with a strong PDSA framework from the Business Rhythm and the involvement of key experts from different levels in an organisation, particularly when it comes to risk identification and mitigation plans, the Standard supports and helps enable multi-level of involvement and ownership. There is, unfortunately plenty of evidence that the Standard is not properly applied, that the key objective is obtaining and keeping the certificate rather than making the intent central to the organisation's approach. IN SBS Transit Rail, we adopted the intent to assist us before seeking certification later.

The result is a single, risk based, integrated management plan based on a clear understanding of performance and condition, informed by insights and experience from different levels within an organisation.

Or, not learning

In one case in 2019 the senior management team of a major suburban Operator decided to ignore the plea from the Operations Control Centre Management team to take specific action to resolve long standing reliability problems in their railway despite them providing detailed analysis highlighting systemic patterns of delays, along with proposed solutions which were supported by expert Train Planners.

By ignoring the plea, the senior management lost the opportunities to improve performance but worse still, to achieve a strong multi layered commitment. The senior management believed they knew best. The senior, experienced staff felt abused and disrespected.

The Importance of good harmonies

In the world's famous choirs, it is the richness of the sum of the voices that makes the sound be mind tingling with the various parts bringing their own unique and distinct contributions.

The high performing organisations are like this too, where the insights and experiences of the parts are bound into a single harmony, nobody being superior or greater than the other, but needing respect and interest to be given to each part played.

In Melbourne in the mid-1990s, Sydney for the Olympics, the start up of the North East Line and Punggol LRT in 2003, and in the reliability revolution in Singapore post 2015 the harmonies came together, pleasing for both the customers, the communities that were served but as importantly for the participants.

The appetite, the Business Rhythm, the discipline all came together.

I came to understand that, as a consequence

The answers to many long term problems are often held inside the organisation

The momentum that is unleashed is very powerful. This creation of five or six levels of aligned leadership, from supervisors who often have excellent insights and experience to the CEO and Boards is a pre-requisite to sustained high performance.

By contrast, if traditional O&M managers continue to use their intuition, (it is called guessing) to identify the improvement initiatives and the required action plans it often results in many unexpected, unwanted 'loss of control' events.

Recognise the different sources of Insight/ownership

It is not unusual for senior managers to recognise that supervisors and front line staff deliver the mission but it is less common to see them as an extremely valuable source of insights and advice.

In my experience from Swansea, Glasgow, Melbourne, Sydney and Singapore having a mission created by Senior Managers is normal but creating a high performing outcome requires involvement and ownership from multiple levels in the team.

When I come across poor performing O&M businesses the senior management's priorities and improvement initiatives are almost always quite different from those that the most experienced font line supervisors and managers would like to see as high priority items on the list of initiatives.

I later read this which reinforced my thinking and practice

In various books, talks and articles Jim Collins highlighted key features of high performing companies including, each of which resonate with my own experience. The ones which resonated with me and my own learning:

- Being great is a matter of choice and discipline.
- Companies that transform do not go about motivating their people. They provide them with an environment where they motivate themselves.
- The review processes involved no blame but only improved understanding of the separable parts and the interdependencies.
- There was an absence of celebrity, no heroes, only the mission. Heroes don't like systems and processes, they love chaos.
- There were no magical identifiable moments. It came from one more step in a long chain of steps, a victory of steadfast discipline.
- Great performance requires the facts to be confronted, not explained away.

If I was starting again, I would adopt this approach.

Create a mission to do something remarkable then create an environment and systems to allow the organisation to own and create the pathway.

Andrew Lezala, a former boss of mine tells a story about going to the Bombardier factory in York UK to celebrate that the factory had won a new train build contract. During his speech he told the delighted staff that they had made a mistake in the bid and that they needed to find 10% savings in the build to avoid losing money, which would not have been good for future work prospects. He challenged the staff to find the savings. Of course, they did it. Nobody had a roadmap just the appetite, curiosity and skill to find a way.

CHAPTER SIX

A skeptical mindset

Managers receive huge amounts of information each month about their business. A key difference between the Process Administrators and by contrast, the Performance Leaders is their willingness to accept an optimistic perspective on how things are going.

While having a well structured hierarchy of meetings is required there is another critical requirement, a skeptical mindset; one which does not take things on face value but one that tests the completeness and basis of the information.

Having a skeptical, questioning rather than an accepting, mindset shapes the culture. The skeptic searches for signs that things are not as good as being reported, that signs of weakness and lack of control are not being reported.

Career observations

Over the past 15 years

In recent years, as an Advisor and/or Reviewer I have attended many meetings and held discussions with many mostly senior managers in Rail O&M organisations outside my own role at SBS Transit between early 2015 and late 2017.

A repeated feature of Business Review meeting was the emphasis by Reporting Managers on claiming that things were well, that performance was good even when the evidence provided suggested that the contrary was true.

Another feature was that the meeting chair was almost always seeking the same thing with very little willingness to challenge what was being reported either verbally or in reports, presentations etc. Discussions after the meetings often led to strong denial when it was pointed out that there might be serious problems. The third-party reviewer is asked to find that things are going well, despite the terms of reference.

Individual discussions tended to be the same.

Poor performing organisations have lots of meetings - even well-structured ones, but these are often characterised by casual acceptance of the norm, combined with a Process Administrator who wants to be able to tick the box, to say that the review was conducted.

Gong through the motions in Review Meetings rather than considering the broader implications of the immediate matter at hand frequently leaves unintended consequences untreated.

These same meetings tend to be characterised as follows:

- Little use of valid trend data or plans to assess or improve underlying performance drivers.
- Little accountability for development transparent improvement plans.
- Little reporting of in-depth investigations into loss of control events, particularly those that happen every day. These events are regarded as inevitable 'noise'.
- That when things have not gone well it has been 'unlucky', not 'our fault'.
- The notion of tomorrow or next year being better was based on hope that 'Special Cause' events will not happen anymore which hasn't been found to be a strong basis for excellence.

A big change in SBS Transit after 2015 was the shift in thinking that delays over 5 minutes are not inevitable, infrequent though they were. The organisation, while being the best performing Line in Singapore for over 5 years was a long way behind MTR in Hong Kong. The Senior Management had become easily satisfied that things were going well even though the causes of 38 of 41 previous delays were due to well-known areas of risk.

Not only that but the promised 3 yearly Rules and Operating Procedure requirement was a mess. The reviews were being reported as being done in that regular and accepted 'tick box' manner, but all in the 36th month rather than in a programme over the three years which would be more in line with the stated intent.

Investigations treated all events as one offs even when there was evidence that there were underlying factors, but it was an environment when the Line Managers were being forced to recommend action plans within hours of the incident before even the most preliminary investigations could be undertaken.

To the skeptical mindset it was clear that beneath the line that distinguished between lagging indicators, loss of control events, and leading indicators, evidence of vulnerability, there was a chasm.

I came to understand that, as a consequence

By 1994, after my years in ScotRail, I had adopted the philosophy that it was management's job to find a way of delivering excellence, that there could be nobody else to blame. That going through the motions as part of the management review process was pointless and boring, where leading indicators showed that things were not as they should be, that more questioning of the facts would reveal significant problems.

For the Sydney Olympic Rail Task then for the startup of the North East Line in Singapore I learned two important lessons:

1. Firstly, that the risk profile in different Rail Organisations are different and that these different risk profiles are not to be used as an excuse for poor outcomes. The job of the O&M Manager is to identify and mitigate the risks. Simple.

2. Secondly, that it is the Senior Management team's job to identify all the risks and challenges and to create a programme that delivers the desired outcomes and mitigates all the foreseeable risks. No excuses.

Under a relatively short-term franchise contract the Contractor is likely to be motivated primarily by improving profit margins while complying with the contract requirements rather than perusing excellence for its own sake. The unintended consequence is a compliant mediocrity.

I later read this which reinforced my thinking and practice

As I re-read the Piper Alpha Inquiry report again, as with other major accident reports, I came to identify the warning signs and lessons that applied in Rail, rather than just within the context of that industry.

Piper Alpha
July 1988 - 167 died

- Senior Management was easily satisfied
  - Easily satisfied that that the PTW was being operated correctly
  - Failed to provide the training required to ensure an effective PTW was operated in practice
  - Adopted a superficial response when issues of safety were raised
  - Failed to ensure that emergency training was being provided

- Permit to work system — short cuts were taken habitually
  - It is essential that staff work exactly to the written procedure
  - Ten steps of the Permit to Work system were frequently departed on
  - The System required 5 further steps

- Documented Training was not delivered
  - Induction training
  - Refresher
  - Drills and exercises

From Lord Cullen's investigation into the Pipa Alpha accident where 167 people were killed when an oil platform exploded in the North Sea off the coast of UK in 1989. From studying this Report, I took two main points of learning.

1. Firstly, that any unexpected failures are evidence of a failure of management; of failure to having identified the risk factors and/or having failed to mitigate those risks.

2. Secondly, that Cullen found that the culture was characterised by complacency and slackness, which is amazing considering the obvious potential consequences of a loss of control event.

It was this thinking that prompted me in 2015 to facilitate a programme with my senior colleagues in SBS Transit in Singapore, to test whether it was possible to operate a railway where the frequency of delays over five minutes was reduced to no more than two per year.

We were not only successful, but the change has been sustained on each of the three SBS Transit Operations in Singapore.

In both Piper Alpha and in SBS Transit Rail, the management had failed to act proactively, to take all reasonable steps to reduce the risk to As Low As Reasonably Practicable (ALARP), let alone SFAIRP.

BP Texas
March 2005 – 15 died

- Warning signs of a possible disaster were present for several years but company officials did not intervene effectively to prevent it – US Chemical Safety and Hazard Investigation Board Report 2007

- Pre-Start-up Safety Review Process to establish that all the required safety checks were done and signed off was not followed

- Individual - 'Employees frequently failed to comply strictly with procedures'

- False Certification - 'Procedures were certified annually as updated and complete by managers but without any attempt to verify with operational staff that procedures were adequate....

- 'For managers compliance with EPA requirements was a matter of urgency while compliance with internal rules and procedures was much more casual.

- Poor Asset and equipment condition was a strong driver of the normal

In 2005, the explosion of an oil refinery in Texas revealed a series of contributing factors where the warning signs had been entrenched and available for interested eyes for some time.

I found that many of these same features are commonly found in Rail O&M Organisations in the late 2010s. With Rail Reliability, Asset performance and condition, compliance with Operating Rules and Procedures etc the warning signs generally present themselves repeatedly with the same trains being late almost every day. Unfortunately, if the overall level of reliability exceeds minimum standards, then the required level of curiosity is curtailed.

In 2016, at Pasir Ris in Singapore two SMRT staff were killed whilst on the track during working hours. The findings are very similar to those of Piper Alpha and BP Texas in respect of management going through the motions but not picking up the embedded non compliance with laid down Rules and Procedures.

As Jim Collins wrote, being great is a matter of choice and discipline.

The mindset.

Key mindset requirement for high performance is what Berkely University found when looking at high performance organisations. Studied highly complex, technology intensive orgnisations that must operate, as far as is humanly possible a failure free standard which seems to be a reasonable starting point for Rail O&M Organisations. If not start there where do you start?

As well as requiring a strong disciplined hierarchy they also found that managers in those high performing organisations were preoccupied with the possibility of failure with expectation of breakdowns and errors rather than an emphasis that shows that all is well.

They also referred to the need for intelligent wariness (skeptical mindset), which requires managers and supervisors always to be looking and testing to see if things are as they appear at first glance.

What a contrast to Piper Alpha, BP in Texas and Pasir Ris. Rail O&M Operators with poor reliability invariably fail to display the characteristics required in Berkely's research even when the potential consequences of any loss of control incidents was obviously high.

If I was starting again, I would adopt this approach.

If I was starting again, I would provide a challenge to align the organisations to do something exceptional and to create a working environment that enables the key insights and experience of the people to bring extra initiatives and new thinking to old problems.

I would confront any acceptance of mediocrity. What do these above accidents tell us about the level of ownership, the level of curiosity and commitment by Senior Managers to proactively identify and mitigate risks?

PART TWO: The Universal Obligations of O&M Managers and the Untrained Industry

The UK's Health and Safety at Work Act 1974 is a great basis on which to form a philosophy with the obligation on managers and employers to take all reasonable steps to reduce the consequence of risks to as low as reasonably practicable. What more guidance do O&M Managers require? My so-called 'universal obligations' emerge from this philosophy, yet the vast majority of O&M Managers remain untrained and unaware of their requirements. This section considers those obligations.

Most O&M Organisations in 2021 refer to their integrated risk management systems covering Safety, Environment, Asset Management, Competence Assurance and Emergency Readiness. While the H&SAWA in various jurisdictions vary only in their text, the expectations and obligations are the same. They became my basis for assessing the maturity of Rail O&M Managers.

I believe that if you are an O&M Manager, you should be able to satisfy these requirements.

- *To be able to demonstrate that you understand performance.*
- *To have documented risks and challenges across different timeframes.*
- *To have resourced mitigation plans for those risks.*

And conversely, if you are not then it seems unlikely that you are meeting your minimum legal obligations.

Between 2017 and 2020 I asked 320 O&M Managers to whom I delivered seminars across several cities and some based in the UK four questions and was astonished at their answers:

- Only 9 had been trained or were able to answer questions regarding valid statistical analytical rules and techniques.
- Only 11 had been trained in how to conduct an investigation.
- Only 6 were aware of the nature of the 'Swiss Cheese' model which brought to life James Reason's contribution to contemporary risk management.
- Only 3 people were aware of the theory of Loss Control and that it is the manager's job to prevent loss of control events – accidents, failures, delays etc.

From this I concluded that the O&M Management proponents are untrained and unskilled. This is not their fault but reflects the dominance of the use of intuition, or guessing by managers, the frequent reliance of key individuals rather than the organisation's policies, systems and processes and the state of 'Learned Helplessness' where industry peers tell themselves and each other that it is not possible for the industry to sustainably perform at a much higher level.

What seems more remarkable is the lack of training for O&M Managers in basic skills. Perhaps this is the main reason for underperformance in so many systems and networks.

I can't think of any group of people in the industry who are so untrained. How have we, as O&M Managers, allowed this obvious weakness to prevail so widely?

In many ways my best boss as a senior manager was Cyril Bleasdale OBE (other buggers' efforts), the first Sector Director for InterCity for British Rail and my supervisor in ScotRail, a great encourager. He was very committed to improving customer service, to find better ways of working and to challenge the status quo.

His obituary in the UK's Railnews in April 2022 referred to Cyril being sent to Stanford University's Executive Programme in the early 1970s. "It changed the way I thought about things and the way I looked at problems. He had been trained to improve his skills at a word leading institution. Outside the new *entrants to Rail, particularly from the military who always seem to have been exposed to many Stanford University type courses, Rail O&M 'lifers' seem to have been left behind. Lucky Cyril and lucky me for having worked for him.*

CHAPTER SEVEN

The difference between running and managing a railway.

Three points.

Firstly, it is common to hear senior O&M managers refer to their "running a railway". These organisations that are 'run' generally perform poorly when compared to the best performers. Senior Managers in the best performing railways more often refer to them managing a system. Running suggests a short term focus dominated by 'chasing their tails', loss of control events, delays and accidents whereas Managing suggests an appreciation of the complex interplay between the various elements of a complete system.

Secondly, in 2013 I was in a discussion with a mentoree who had made a significant difference to the performance of the team he was leading. During the discussion he said that he thought he'd done a great job and that he wanted to look for a bigger challenge within the business. I asked him what would happen in his area if he left today. He replied that within six months it would be back where he was when he arrived, so I suggested that he hadn't in fact achieved anything, which he thought was a bit harsh but it did make me reflect on my career with a more critical perspective.

I had enjoyed many career highlights up to that point but I did wonder about the permanence of the impact I had made.

Thirdly, when I went back to SBS Transit Rail in 2015, after a gap of nine years, unsurprisingly some of the things we had put in place had fallen by the wayside some of which had, I thought been well regarded. As a consequence, for my second term every member of the senior team had a veto regarding any proposed new initiatives, processes or systems on the basis that it would be a waste of all of our time if we developed and implemented a series of changes only for them to stop if and when I got knocked off my bike, so to speak.

It made our deliberations much more interesting and helped me to adopt the role as a facilitator and enabler rather than the single guiding mind. The results were incredible. I am told that all the processes and systems are still in place after four years with the three Lines and System operating at a level of reliability regarded as impossible back in 2015 with only one or two delays over five minutes per year.

This is what managing looks like. Clear structures, accountabilities and entrenched effective processes and systems which involve multiple levels of leadership, each bring their unique insights and experience to bear.

Career observations

As a Duty Manager at Victoria Station in London between 1985 and 1987 that it became apparent that there were strong patterns within the overall network, 'common events'. The same things went wrong almost every day with other 'special events' in a haphazard way.

As managers we seemed to be obsessed about the 'special events' but completely unaware of the 'common events' that occurred every day. The subsequent analysis showed that sustainable higher performance was available if we resolved those 'common events'.

It was also apparent that the very experienced senior supervisors needed no assistance in handling the 'special events' because they had seen it all before over the years. I realised that it was the Managers job to analyse and resolve the 'common events'; that it was me and my colleagues' job to understand and manage the system.

Reacting v Managing

Understanding and mitigating risks
Act on causes not the consequential events

The safety outcome hierarchy   The reliability outcome hierarchy

• Runners, or reactors, typically look at the outcomes, the lagging indicators of loss of control.

• Managers tend to look at the leading indicators, the predictors of the outcomes.

• Scrutiny and understanding of the controllables rather than the outcomes are where the answers to finding the pathway to high performance is to be found

This concept was never taught this but this blindness to the patterns was also apparent later in Scotland, Melbourne and Singapore. The supervisors ran the System, whatever it threw up at them, for better or worse but it was the Manager's job to understand and adjust the system, to make it easier for the senior supervisors to deliver excellent performance.

The traditional approach of top down running the railway failed but that was what we were encouraged to do: emulating our predecessors examples.

I came to understand that, as a consequence

Runners have certain characteristics

- Very reactive, very hierarchical, 'brains off at the gate', do what you are told.
- A tendency to have poorly developed organisational processes and systems, unremarkable performance at best and a very high personality dependence.

One CEO of a major Australian System told me in 2008 that 'there was no delegated authority for decision making. I am in charge of everything'. He must have had remarkable insight!

The idea of 'running' an organisation suggests an old fashioned 'top down, do as I say', personality-dependent culture which has been shown does not lead to sustainable high performance.

It is the shift supervisors and their teams that run railways. The others are part of the overall system that enables the runners to be successful. When

Senior Management direct, they are frequently wrong which is hardly surprising. Lots of intuition, or guessing!

It is common for these senior managers to determine what actions should be taken to prevent the recurrence of an unwanted, unexpected loss of control event after only the most preliminary investigation having been carried out.

The real danger of this approach is that the multiples of people with deep knowledge, insight and experience learn that complying with the poor directives becomes the overriding objective. Sight is lost of the more realistic and overall intent that all 'reasonable steps' should be taken to prevent recurrence. It is not generally their fault. They have not been trained, the industry has failed them and, as a consequence, their stakeholders.

Managers, also have common characteristics

- Managing requires an emphasis on analysis and proactive risk identification and mitigation. Managing should be focused on improving the effectiveness of their systems, helping the people to find and institutionalise the most effective ways of working.

- High Performance requires insights and experience from multiple levels to sustain high performance. High Performance also requires understanding based on proper, valid analysis. Railways are generally rich in data but information poor.

- The creation of multi part harmonies where multiple layers of the organisation work together: Collaboration and Cooperation is essential. Good governance enables this and enables issues to be raised for discussion and evaluation

Managing requires a deep understanding and experience of system thinking. Nobody taught me that and I find it is usually missing in O&M Managers skill sets or understanding.

The lack of basic competence in the industry, even so far as legal obligations, is widespread, made worse by adopting the approach taken by senior managers who have suffered from the same lack of training along with the common Groupthink which minimises personal accountability.

In the next section we explore the Universal Obligations of O&M Managers before looking at four specific but critical areas where the industry is untrained in Part Three. Without an understanding and competence in the Universal Obligations the claim to be professional is weak with mediocre performance remaining the norm.

I later read this which reinforced my thinking and practice

The Queensland Rail Train Crewing Practices, Commission of Inquiry, January 2017

The Inquiry was set up to look at how the requirement for additional train drivers had been dealt with by Queensland Rail for the opening of a new Line to Moreton Bay in 2016. Phillip Strachan made some findings that seemed to sum up much of what I had and continued to observe in Rail O&M Managers.

These include:

- 'There was a culture of complacency and reluctance for sharing bad news'
- An over-reliance on intuition at the expense of using data (Guessing)
- A culture of complacency rather than taking proactive steps to understand and address the causes of operational issues

---

If I was starting again, I would adopt this approach.

I would try to guide the managers to understand that they need to be proactive and disciplined in their thinking and action, that 'running' is doomed to be reactive while 'managing is about understanding, proactive and therefore preventing 'loss of control' events.

An understanding of contributing factors is essential which requires an appreciation of system thinking, something that came to me quite late in my career.

Looking back, I found that there were very few incidents of 'loss of control' where the event or its consequences could not have been avoided whether related to reliability or safety performance.

CHAPTER EIGHT

Understanding Loss Control Theory

Career observations

From my research between 2017 and 2020 only 3 out of 320 Rail O&M managers were familiar with the concept of Loss Control. Frank Bird (1970) developed Loss Control Theory and suggested that underlying cause of loss of control, accidents, delays or breakdowns, are lack of management controls and poor management decisions. Later writers including Reason, with the Swiss Cheese model and Lord Cullen in the Piper Alpha Inquiry support this.

It was George Barclay, an experienced safety expert in ScotRail who taught me about the responsibility of being proactive to create prevention

He helped me to understand that if we thought about it, we knew who the poor staff were, we knew where the real risks were including where the Rules and Procedures were unworkable and that our primary responsibility was to be proactive.

He got me to understand that management arrangements were the designed barriers to prevent unwanted, unexpected, unplanned events and that if they were poorly designed or applied it was not the staff's fault but managements.

He explained this as the concept of Loss Control. I found him to be an intelligent thinker and certainly he helped me with my own development.

I came to understand that, as a consequence

The manager's job is to avoid loss of control. George helped me to internalise that as an O&M Manager I was aware of where the risks were, who the people in ScotRail's Operations team needed assistance and who in previous roles had been 'at risk' signalmen, drivers etc. He got me to understand that knowing and not acting was reckless, that knowing and not acting was wholly unprofessional.

From our discussions, my reading and reflections I came to internalise that having a skeptical mindset is essential. That what Lord Cullen observed at Piper Alpha about senior management being easily satisfied that things were as they should be was both common and evidence of refusing to scrutinise or really look.

As such, George Barclay provided a candid but refreshing perspective into my obligations. He became a rejected prophet in Scotland but why? Too many O&M managers didn't seem to welcome the refreshing perspective which crystalised what 'taking all reasonable steps meant'.

I later read this which reinforced my thinking and practice

Later, and still, I read many major accident inquiries and others, such as reports into the   shambles of the launch of Thameslink in London in 2018 and Queensland Rail's 2017 Inquiry which shed light on the problems of the prevailing mindset, most of which reflects the power and weakness of untrained incompetence and Groupthink.

We ought to be much better than that.

If I was starting again, I would adopt this approach.

The concept of loss of control is interesting because it provides a broader context than the normal mantras provide such as 'safety is always first' or 'the customer is king'. It provides a philosophy that goes across all the disciplines and highlights a key role for managers. To ensure that the management-determined processes aiming to prevent loss (accidents, delays, loss of competence, loss of emergency readiness etc) require detailed review and monitoring to ensure that the defences against loss are effective and healthy.

This requires not only training but also promotion and encouragement, not only for new Managers but, as we did in Swansea with the Alcohol Initiative, a team-based learning on our roles and responsibilities. Leaving this to individual crusade or bottom-up persuasion is unlikely to be effective.

In today's (2020s) railways we seem to spend more time and money on accrediting leaders through training programmes. It might be better to help these people become competent first and then see who emerges as the leaders?

CHAPTER NINE

Bringing the Legal Requirements for O&M Managers to Life

Introduction

Afternoon working in various capacities over almost 40 years I concluded that there is only one task for all Rail O&M Managers encompassing the key role. This conclusion has been tested with many old colleagues and confidence in its veracity holds.

- The systematic, proactive identification and mitigation of risk

So, why haven't I ever heard it explained like that?

In a sense, it is these reflections that have motivated me to write this book, to share insights and experience that I wish somebody had taught me when I was 30.

Experienced O&M Managers are often very knowledgeable about aspects of their networks but often have a poor understanding of how they work as a system.

Their inability to know how to conduct analysis prevents them from understanding their systems or, consequently from being able to intervene to improve the system on a sustainable basis.

Sustained High performance requires managers and organisations to have a Management System. This applies to safety, environment, reliability, competence, emergency readiness, finance etc.

This and the next section attempt to unpack the layers of the onion, moving from the single focus of risk identification and mitigation into the six universal obligations of high performing Rail O&M managers.

Is safety really the top priority?

This became a popular saying in the UK in 1990 after the series of multiple fatality accidents over the previous 3 years – Zeebrugge, Kings Cross, Piper Alpha, Clapham etc – but in the ensuing 30 years the approach to risk identification and mitigation has become more sophisticated.

While 'safety is our top priority' has a neat ring to it profitability is the purpose for most business' being. When 2020s Rail O&M managers say safety is our top priority, further inquiry usually reveals a lack of understanding of the either their legal requirements or how this translates into a well-structured framework which systematically and proactively maintains their understanding of performance, the associated risks and the required mitigation plans. An untrained industry – more of that later.

If safety is their top priority, then their underlying approach to all matters of risk should be the same. I believe there should be lots of evidence that the systematic, proactive identification and mitigation of risk is a key philosophy underpinning the approach to all matters including reliability, asset condition, competence, systems of work, emergency readiness etc. Can one logically apply such an approach to only one element of your work? To me it seems unlikely.

A quick analysis of the requirement provides a myriad of areas where risks and their mitigation needs to be addressed. Perhaps it is the size of this onerous commitment that puts people off? Perhaps it is that most Rail O&M managers have not been trained properly or their own leaders have not displayed the appetite or the capacity to show them?

Career observations since 2017

In London the terrazzo tiles installed at Waterloo and Victoria Stations (and many others) were found to be dangerously slippery when wet has resulted in a very high number of serious passenger slips and falls and yet, 30 years later, the problem has been left unresolved because, presumably, somebody has done an analysis that says that not enough people get hurt badly enough.

This contrasts with the Ponte della Constituzione in Venice, a footbridge over the Grand Canal near Venice Station opened in 2008. It had two glass 'pathways' each side of a narrow concrete central path, aimed at symbolizing Venice's embrace of modernity.

Ponte della Constituzione, Venice

- Opened in 2008 with mostly glass pathways.
- While a 'thing of beauty' the bridge became associated with daily stories of tumbles and dangerous slips
- Soon after opening the locals would only walk on the narrow central concrete pathway to avoid slipping.
- After a decade of ineffective glass treatments the decision was made to remove the glass in 2018.
- They acted and addressed the route cause, unlike in the London Stations at Waterloo and Victoria.

Similarly, also in the UK, I note the unresolved problems with disc brake trains slipping, after over 30 years, sometimes for long distances, where the driver has no control. The M&EE were able to transfer the significant residual risk to the civil engineer's tree cutting down programme and the operations staff. Is that really the best that they could come up with?

Elsewhere, new Metro Lines have been opened for passenger services without safety-critical technical systems being commissioned, Operating Rules and Procedures being known to be incomplete, inadequate staff available to meet emergency management plan requirements on underground stations.

In respect of reliability, reviews have identified established patterns of delays identified by using basic applied statistical analysis, but senior managers have ignored the evidence and pushed ahead with pre-determined, uninformed decisions.

Are any of these organisations putting the proactive, systematic identification and mitigation of risks first? It seems unlikely but they all state that 'safety is their top priority'!

I came to understand that, consequently:

The requirements of high O&M performance are laid down in the Health and Safety Legislation, certainly in the UK, Canada, Australia and Singapore. This became clear to me when I realised that almost all 'loss of control events', delays, asset failures and accidents resulted from well known factors coming together.

Similarly, these legal obligations are the basis of the ISO 55,001 Asset Management standard and the Australian Rail Safety Standard, AS 4292.

The requirements are as follows:

- That O&M Managers must be able to demonstrate that they understand performance, if only so that they can comply with the second requirement regarding the identification of risks.
- O&M Managers must be able to identify the risks and challenges that they need to manage
- That the potential consequences of these risks must be mitigated, and the consequence reduced to SFAIRP, So Far As Is Reasonably Practicable.

It seems reasonable that these obligations apply to any 'loss of control' events whether safety, reliability, asset condition or performance, emergency readiness, competence assurance etc. It was a related discussion in Singapore in 2015 when the senior Rail team in SBS Transit agreed that we had not taken all reasonable steps regarding known factors which had resulted in 21 delays over 5 minutes in each of the previous two years. The challenges were to enhance our understanding of performance and conditions and to become proactive to prevent any of the foreseeable delays, 'loss of control events', from occurring.

Business Continuity Management (BCM)

BCM has three pillars;

- The management of functional risk through prevention activities by maintenance teams.
- Failure containment by operations staff.
- Recovery, usually operations led with support from maintainers.

The significance of this for O&M managers is the relationship between the operations and the maintenance teams for managing the whole task.

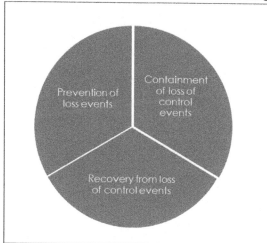

It has become fashionable for BCM to be seen as a separate and specific activity by Rail managers whereas in high performing organisations such as those found in Hong Kong and Singapore the elements of BCM are embedded in the approach to the daily tasks.

If I was starting again, I would adopt this approach.

Two key issues seem to be worth highlighting.

Firstly, I would ensure that these three obligations of O&M Management were understood at various levels in organisations to the extent that supervisors and managers, particularly senior managers appreciated what it meant for them and their accountabilities. I would also ensure that the managers felt competent and confident about discharging their responsibilities.

The next three Chapters are aimed at providing more background about these three areas.

Secondly, I would ensure that O&M managers understood the basic requirements of BCM with a particular emphasis that a BCM is not separate from daily work but is an integral underlying principle behind high performance and high readiness.

CHAPTER TEN

Understanding Performance

*A*fter *Appetite for excellence, and perhaps the appointment of suitably experienced, qualified managers, I regard the need to be understand performance and condition as the next critical issue.*

To be able to effectively identify and mitigate risks requires the O&M Manager to be able to provide a transparent, valid basis of how they assure themselves about performance.

If an O&M Manager can not demonstrate the basis on which they assure themselves that things are OK I believe it is unlikely that their risk identification processes are sound.

In a later section I cover Analysis and Understanding. Unfortunately, most O&M Managers are untrained and unaware of how to conduct valid analysis so typically draw conclusions from unsound, invalid reports. As a result, consequential decisions and actions are usually unsound resulting in no sustained improvement resulting in a sense of Learned Helplessness. More of that later.

Career observations

Throughout my career, everywhere that I have worked there has been a lack of knowledge of repeating patterns of failure whether in the performance of Operating Groups or Sectors of services which share tracks or within the sub systems of any asset class, despite there being entrenched patterns and interdependencies for those who were curious enough to look.

Early Years

In 1985 while Traffic Manager at Ipswich, UK I learned about the patterns and dependencies from two perspectives.

Firstly, to ensure that the growing number of Freightliner trains were able to be operated out of the largest container port in England, Felixstowe each evening we recognised that the key moments were at about 1400. If the key moving parts of the whole chain were not in place at that time heavy intervention was required. After that it became too late recognising that the line had three single line sections and only two short passing loops. There was a system to be observed and managed to enable the desired outcomes to be delivered.

Secondly, ensuring that London bound trains left on time was critical to ensuring that the train paths for trains closer to London were not compromised recognising that the availability of smooth train paths for trains from Clacton, Colchester and Southend Victoria were not compromised.

In both cases the quality of the final outcomes were dependent on the precise execution of the plan some hours beforehand. My introduction to leading indicators.

Later Years

While conducting a review of a major Operator in the late 2010s in 2019 I asked several senior managers in operations about the variability of reliability between the different Groups. None was aware of any significant variation, yet the two worst Groups operated under 80% within 5 minutes in peak periods while two of the others were very close to 90%.

In three railways in four jurisdictions between 2018 and 2019 I was invited to attend the monthly reliability meeting in each place. The shocking thing was the absence of any systematic analysis or report on trends. The reliance on anecdotes to describe past performance was common to each with no systematic assessment of status or progress. In each case the managers believed that excellent performance was beyond the system capability. Hope but no action prevailed.

Without exception well regarded, experienced O&M Managers frequently do not know about or understand the repeating patterns of failure and as a consequence their entrenched ideas of how things should be improved are often invalid.

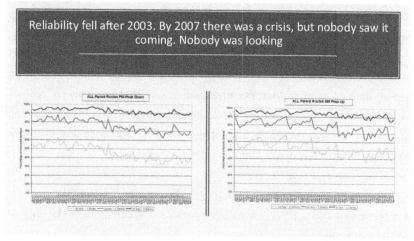

Reliability fell after 2003. By 2007 there was a crisis, but nobody saw it coming. Nobody was looking

The Table above shows the peak hour reliability in Melbourne's network between 2000 and 2008. The patterns of decline in reliability are clear. When broken down into the Operating Groups, each with their own patterns what was happening was obvious.

Based on my experience in many Networks in several countries this clarity of patterns is both normal and revealing at network, train service group and line level and the managers are generally unaware of them.

Victoria Station and London's Southern Region in the 1980s

As had been my practice at Ipswich when branch line trains missed their London connections as a Duty Manager at Victoria, I made it my business to be close to the ticket barrier line, with my lovely gold braided hat, when services from the affected platforms were delayed or cancelled. It hadn't been the practice of my colleagues, so I received a brutal reception.

Over the weeks and months, what became apparent was that the same trains were delayed or cancelled almost every day. There were distinct patterns. These were caused by what I later came to understand as Common Causes. They were part of the system, and because they were part of the normal system, they were masked in the focus on the daily average performance. They didn't stand out, unlike major Special Cause failure events which attracted management follow-up attention because they stood out.

It became obvious that if the Common Cause patterns could be resolved the overall daily average would rise and perhaps the customers would stop being so aggressive.

While the patterns in the evening peak were the most apparent feedback from customers revealed that there were patterns in the morning too. I soon had 20 data collectors. What became evident was that the daily collapse of service patterns, in two distinct waves approaching Victoria in the morning was caused by an unworkable timetable of the East Grinstead line and slack working at Epsom every morning,

In the later discussions senior managers became angry when the analysis was presented and both local Area Managers were in complete denial regarding the evidence.

ScotRail in the early 1990s

As we began our reliability journey all of the Line Managers were asked to nominate the repeating issues that prevented a 100% on time delivery every day. What came to light was that all their insights were based on accepted wisdom but were completely unfounded when they were asked to provide the data justifying their opinions.

This kicked off a series of analyses by Line Managers of what were the repeating problems since the special cause events reported themselves. What emerged was that every time the analysis focused on a particular line the performance improved a lot.

We discovered that the highest impact problems were the execution of the timetable or problems with the operability of the timetable. Nothing much has changed in that regard in the subsequent 30 years as I have worked from place to place.

Melbourne 1994 to 1997

The 'known causes' of Melbourne's performance problems were apparently well known by everybody, except they were shown to be incorrect once some high level analysis was conducted.

On arriving in Melbourne in 1994 I was told very assertively by the Operations Team that there was nothing wrong with the timetable design but that all the problems were caused by the unreliable trains. The Trains Maintenance team told me they needed to replace the whole traction system since that was the major reliability problem and if not, there was nothing much that could be done.

The peak reliability for about a decade had been about 86% within 5 minutes. There was a sense of helplessness rather than denial. Thankfully, as with the ScotRail team, the appetite was high.

What soon transpired was that a high-level analysis showed that the timetable was unworkable in one of the four sectors of the network. Three sectors performed at a ten-year average close to 90% while one of the four sectors operated at approximately 78%. The same trains were delivering 90% in three sectors as the 78%. It was due to the timetable design and its operability.

With the trains we found that a myriad of low-cost improvements on doors, air conditioning etc and some work place changes on how train faults were treated significantly improved train reliability.

After the timetable change in 1996 these changes led to a peak hour reliability of 93% in 1996/97 and a promise of a sustainable peak reliability over 95% after the rationalisation of the track layout and work practices in central Melbourne. This was duly achieved after 2001 for a few years until external events introduced a period of instability and some loss of control.

As with ScotRail's managers, everybody was wrong, but the execution and operability of the timetable design were the two high impact problems.

Between 2017 and 2019, when conducting deep Independent Reviews of reliability in five networks in four countries, the findings were almost exactly the same. What differed each time was the management's response to the analysis.

I also observed this

A revolution was possible. Basic analysis provides many aha moments of realisation

Melbourne 1994:

The main problem was the design and operability of the timetable, not the trains. To the extent it was the trains there was a great deal of low hanging fruit without dealing with what the collective mindset had agreed was the main issue and without resolving that, nothing could be achieved.

The evidence was staring us in the face but the inability to properly analyse the trend data coupled with the entrenched group think prevented the managers from seeing.

SBS Transit 2016+

While the proper use and analysis of data was a key part of the journey, creating multiple owners and champions of the new work processes was identified as being critical to prevent the old way of working returning once a change in Business Head occurred.

Giving each member of the senior team a veto card as we developed our new processes and systems, which was used occasionally, enabled there to be several champions of the changes. This has enabled the new processes and systems to remain in place.

With two changes in Business Head since 2017 the appetite for excellence and the Business Rhythm have remained largely unchanged. The MacDonald's like, disciplined processes and systems seem to be entrenched.

I came to understand that, as a consequence.

Sector or Group Patterns

Each suburban railway displays a pattern of regular delays, often with different service groups or sectors within the same network having very different patterns and statistical system characteristics, each of which need to be understood and addressed. A one solution plan will not work.

In Sydney with three sectors, Melbourne with five, Perth with three and Brisbane with two, an analysis has shown this to be the case yet in each city the senior management tend only to look at the overall number rather than analysing each sector's performance which would inevitably lead to questions regarding the difference.

My recollection from the UK is that Glasgow has three electric train service groups, Victoria in London two on each of the Southern and Central sides.

Statistical Analysis

Everywhere I have worked and reviewed when it comes to reliability, I have found that the Common Cause problems lie with the incompatibility of the timetable with the infrastructure layout and repeated local lack of discipline issues. Well over 98% of the problems lie there with Special Cause events also having a very specific impact but only when they occur.

In statistical analysis terms, the O&M Managers job is to understand the patterns and the statistical capabilities of these systems before embarking on a journey to improve performance by improving the arithmetic mean of the performance and by reducing the variability.

Together they combine to improve predictability and customer satisfaction whilst also reducing anxiety that comes from that sense that operating suburban railways are 10 challenges per week. They are not. There is only one timetable, the management's plan.

The tables below shows that the PM Peak average reliability for the period looked at operated at 86.5% but with the different Groups ranging from 93.8% to 77.9%.

The 93.8% Group has a low range or variation compared to the other Groups, is statistically stable and much more predictable than the others. The challenge for the Operations and Planners is to understand what causes these differences. Never mind overall averages, the management challenge is within each Group.

In Sydney Sector two has been the long-standing problematic Sector with Sector One being the most stable and highest performing, while in Melbourne the Clifton Hill Group has tended to be the best with the Northern and Cross City being the most challenging.

The analysis in Glasgow was the same in the 1990s. The Argyle Line remained a challenge while the North and South Electrics were high performing and stable.

In your railway, which are the most and least stable Groups?

Each of the Operating Groups or Sectors shown below has different statistical characteristics.

- Different arithmetic means
- Different limits of variation.

The Special Cause days are obvious with days where performance was below or very close to the Lower Control Limits, but the overall average/arithmetic mean performance within each Group is driven by the common cause events - those events which are systematic and are not obvious without proper analysis.

These common causes within each Group need to be analysed and treated separately to improve each Group, to improve the overall Network performance. Experience suggests that poorer performing Groups have a timetable whose operability is compromised by the timetable design and the infrastructure layout combined with poor operating disciplines.

The graphs below illustrate five Groups or Sectors from one Railway for the evening peak period with arithmetic mean performance varying between 77% and 90%. None of them very good but importantly all quite different in their variability and mean (average) performance.

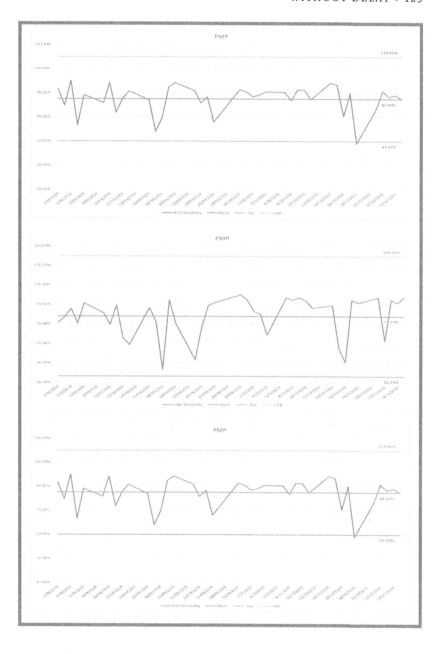

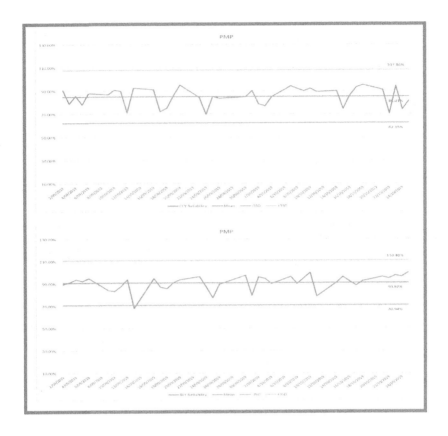

Metro Operations

Experience from both SBS Transit and SMRT in Singapore, including their respective Mass Transit and Light Rail Systems shows that while timetables are much simpler than with suburban railways within the different asset classes there are distinct patterns of failures at sub system and key component level which provide those managers with the same opportunity as the suburban Operators.

The role of the Maintenance Manager is to reduce the mean level of failure at sub system and key component level – prevention activity. The role of the Operations Manager is to reduce the impact of the failure through effective containment and then recovery, bringing together the three pillars of BCM.

Together the capacity of the team to collaborate to reduce both the risks and the impact of failures is very powerful.

The example below illustrates the power of valid applied statistical analysis.

It highlights the system's characteristics in terms of stability and predictability, the arithmetic mean improving with the successful implementation of a change in the Planned Maintenance scope and schedule.

It shows quite clearly that the mean level of failure has been reduced as has the predictability and stability of the sub system. These are the two critical objectives of the Maintenance Manager.

As importantly, this methodology also improves both understanding and transparency.

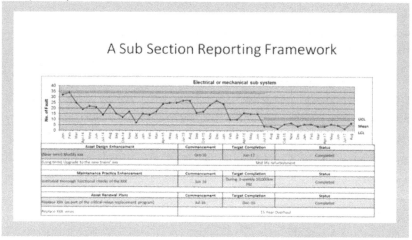

The table also shows the three categories of intervention.

- Enhance the design.
- Change out of components.
- Change to the scope and/or frequency of Planned Maintenance (PM) activities.

In this case the big improvement came from changes in the PM – they were almost free, as is often the case. More effective prevention of loss of control events.

The table below shows how train door failures were reduced on a System where previously the management had stated that there was nothing that could be done without replacing all the assets.

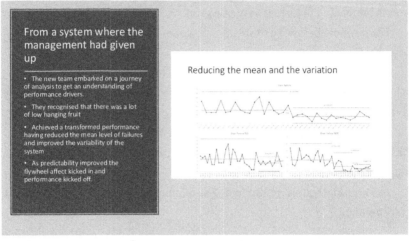

Invalid use of trend data is common by O&M Managers

I have seen many reports and sat through many presentations where graphs with perhaps 12 data points are shown with perhaps two or three data points of recent improvement often leading to comments of a congratulatory nature. These improvements are usually false dawns because the basis of the analysis is invalid. What is being observed is just the normal variation of within a system.

> Graphs with inadequate data points to make any valid conclusions are common. A minimum of 25 or 30 is required and 7 points above or below a mean, or 7 points in succession are required before any statistically valid claim can be made

Why is it so rare to see this? It reflects a lack of training and promotion of senior managers of valid practices. This capacity and capability deficit not only applies to O&M Managers at various levels but also Owners, State Agencies and Regulators.

There is a great deal of evidence of invalid practices, driven and allowed by senior people. Consequently, this example permeates the 'way we do things here', the culture. Learned Helplessness becomes entrenched.

Management Training regarding valid statistical analysis has not been done

How could all the managers be so wrong and unaware in London, Scotland and Melbourne despite the managers assuming that they are amazingly knowledgeable about their networks?

The Total Quality Management training in Melbourne in 1995 provided by Dr Jackie Graham of Statistical Edge, in conjunction with a disciplined and sufficiently skeptical and curious Business Rhythm of review meetings triggered an enormous improvement in performance and a sense of pride and confidence in the broader team and workforce. It was the same in Singapore 20 years later.

The managers and supervisors had not been trained to conduct analysis. Their understanding was based on entrenched Groupthink resulting in a sense of learned helplessness.

We learned the significant benefit from basic applied statistical analysis, not only as a basis of much improved performance but also of improved capability, pride and ambition.

If a manager does not know how to conduct valid statistical analysis it is likely that any conclusions drawn from either analysis, or a report will be invalid. As a consequence, drawing invalid conclusions from analysis and studying investigation reports is common resulting in action plans which do not deliver sustained improvement.

Much of what is known to be true is based invalid analysis, highlighting the cultural isolation that Rail O&M managers have from contemporary management practices.

The power of valid applied statistical analysis

Valid Applied Statistical Analysis is not tricky to either conduct of apply but there are rules to be adhered to ensure that the analysis is both accurate and valid.

In each case that I have seen it applied, it has led to many initiatives which have resulted in a dramatic and sustainable improvement in performance with reduced arithmetic means and reduced variation, even when the situation had become accepted as impossible to do anything about.

The analysis helps managers and supervisors to get a single and valid understanding of the truth and, unless constrained, results in the experts at several levels of an organisation developing and implementing improvement initiatives.

It was this approach underpinned the transformed reliability In SBS Transit's North East Line and Sengkang-Punggol LRT systems after 2015 and SMRT's Bukit Panjang LRT after 2018.

Unfortunately, there are other examples where analysis showed that the previously held and entrenched opinions about underlying factors driving performance were not accepted and the managers chose to drive forward on their pre-determined pathway. They failed to deliver any improvement. Disappointing but validating and perhaps almost reassuring.

There is a tendency to focus on 'Special Cause' events rather than 'Common Cause' patterns

What is the difference?

A 'Common Cause' is a systemic cause, something that typically goes unnoticed in the daily operation because it is normal 'noise'. They need to be identified by proper systemic analyses leaving the challenge of the owning manager to work out how to reduce the mean level of failure and to reduce the variation, and as a consequence, improve predictability.

A 'Special Cause' is an event which is not caused by systemic events. They tend to be quite dramatic in nature. They require a specific analysis and prevention action plan because they are not systemic.

Special Cause are higher profile than common causes

When there is major asset failure or passenger incident the Administrators become convinced that these issues are the major problems which everybody can see and therefore understand.

It's all part of the Groupthink domination based on laziness, low appetite and incompetence reflecting a lack of training.

Why do O&M Managers seem to prefer to focus on Special Causes?

Special Cause events tend to have a bigger impact when they occur than Common Cause events. They present an 'action man' aura which is easily explained and appreciated by Boards, Regulators etc.

In each Network reviewed over a decade the repeating focus on Special Cause, non-systemic events, rather than the common causes, the daily failures, suggests that the common causes are of little interest to managers even though they are their controllables which can make so much difference.

Unfortunately, the lack of focus on common causes is usually reflected with poor performance due to a lack of understanding on identifying and acting on Common Causes. Despite widely held views to the contrary it is the understanding and managing of Common Cause events that leads to sustained performance improvement.

A Case Study: UK, Strategic Rail Authority (SRA) Study on Reliable Capacity, for Suburban Railways

The SRA sponsored a study by Birmingham University which was published in 2003. It introduced a critical concept: that capacity and reliability should be considered together as a single concept. No point in promising more train per hour capacity if it makes the rest of the system unreliable, which happened in Sydney with the infamous November 1996 timetable which its designers described as 'tight'. It could work reliably but very rarely does.

The Study revealed three key findings:

- That adding more trains up to 80% of the theoretical capacity did not cause any reduction in network reliability.

- That beyond 80% reliability fell away, all other things being equal, as the network became more congested.
- That beyond 90% it fell very dramatically, all other things being equal, with the secondary impacts of any delays cascading through the Sector.

Three key points emerge from this.

- This model has been used by Rail O&M Managers to explain that reliability fell because they run more trains. This is a frequent but flawed assertion in my opinion, since it is based on an assumption that dismisses the universal obligation that the manager's job is to proactively identify and mitigate risk. It allows a Groupthink to emerge that it's not our fault, that it is unreasonable to expect any better.
- If the task becomes more complex, and this is known that extra care in the discipline around timetable execution is required, not only by the operational staff but by the Maintainer too, to enable a tighter but more precise plan to be delivered.
- Since reliability targets are usually based on an up to 5 minutes late standard it is common for O&M managers to think that anything up to 5 minutes late is acceptable. The problem is that this ignores the Timetable Designers working which assumes that train paths are only 30 seconds wide and that as railways get busier their implementation must become more precise. The Study highlights the growing lack of tolerance for even minor delays as the Networks become busier and the consequential imperative for operational disciplines to become more precise.

I came to understand the importance of the mindset and the culture.

In many railways the prevailing attachment to 'trying hard', mediocre expectations and low accountability seems to be deeply entrenched.

Learned Helplessness (not knowing how to look) and/or Denial (a refusal to look) are both common. 'It doesn't matter what we do, the game does not change, the dial refuses to move' is a common conclusion to discussions with experienced O&M managers.

Despite some O&M Managers being presented with valid statistical analysis there remains many examples of the reliance on intuition or guessing.

The drivers and consequences of 'Organisational Culture' are considered in Part Four of this book.

The Untrained Industry

My research between 2017 and 2020 revealed that only 9 out of 320 O&M Managers had been trained and were knowledgeable and competent to conduct valid applied statistical analysis. As a consequence, the tendency to rely on invalid opinions seems to prevail or the dominant example provided by untrained leaders. As a consequence, the warning signs which are often staring managers in the face are missed or ignored.

What the Melbourne in the 1990s, the SBS Transit Rail improvement in the post 2016 period and the Bukit Panjang LRT transformation reveals is that once trained, given the appropriate appetite and governance disciplines the latent capability of the teams can be easily realised.

What Justice Sheen, who led the Zeebrugge Inquiry in 1987, called "the disease of sloppiness" can be addressed. The casual acceptance of frequent avoidable loss of control events, learned helplessness, can be changed by training the O&M Managers.

If O&M Managers do not know how to conduct or review analysis, they are unable to properly understand the characteristics of their systems' performance and effectively intervene to deliver improvement.

I later read this which reinforced my thinking and practice
<u>Edward Deming's Theory of Profound Knowledge.</u>

Edward Deming is seen by many as the founding father of Total Quality Management (TQM) who is commonly regarded as the shaper of the Japanese industrial revolution after WW2.

He promoted the concept of quality ahead of production, the avoidance of error and mistakes, to reduce waste, to reduce supervision and checks to create highly successful production systems.

He identified four key functions of his learning which he brought together in his Theory of Profound Knowledge:

- Appreciation for a system

Action in one part of a system, an organisation or Business, has an impact on other parts of the system. These unintended consequences are reduced when managers understand the nature of systems.

- Knowledge about variation.

Deming identified that one goal of quality is to reduce variation or improve predictability of outcome. He recognised two types of variation; those that happen inside the system and those that happen outside the system, common and special causes which require quite different treatment.

Without his understanding Deming concluded that managers who do not understand variation often make things worse by their actions.

- Theory of knowledge.

Deming claimed that there is no knowledge without theory, that theory requires prediction, not just explanation. Rail O&M managers are big on explanation but are frequently untrained and unfamiliar regarding theory.

- Knowledge of psychology.

Deming requires managers to understand how people learn, relate to change and what motivates them.

Reflections on Demming

I agree with a key Deming assertion that profound knowledge is only useful if it is invited and received with an eagerness to learn and improve. He also believed that prior experiences often create biased obstacles to learning and improving.

The challenges about reliance on entrenched bias and the openness, or not, to learning and improving will be looked at later but it raises significant cultural traits and their impact on risk identification and mitigation.

An investigation into the UK's Mid Staffordshire Health Authority in 2013 by Robert Francis into a poorly performing hospital found that people called to give evidence at the Public Inquiry used the term hindsight 123 times and 'with the benefit of hindsight' 378 times'. He found that the warning signs were staring them in the face. 501 times!

He concluded that the main issues were cultural and included the following:

- A lack of openness to criticism.
- An acceptance of poor standards and,
- A failure to put patients first.

He concluded that the problems were found to be cultural, not medical.

The hindsight reference was particularly revealing. The evidence was staring interested eyes in the face. The problems were glaringly obvious.

- Did the managers know about the problems? No but the information was available for interested eyes.
- Did the managers and Regulators conduct analysis to help enhance understanding? No
- Why not? An untrained industry?

These findings were very similar to other UK Health Sector Investigations with the investigation into very high cardiac mortality rates at St George's Hospital in London in 2013 and into deaths of 29 babies undergoing heart surgery at Bristol Royal Infirmary in1998.

In the Bristol case the Inquiry lifted the lid on an 'old boy's' culture among doctors; patients being left in the dark about their treatment; a lax approach to clinical safety; low priority given to children's services; secrecy about doctor's performance, and a lack of external monitoring of NHS performance. It could have been a Rail O&M organisation with poor reliability performance.

In the Mid Staffordshire case there was a "defensive approach on data on deaths". "It is a worry that things were allowed to progress so far without senior management getting a grip". Again, the problems were seen as cultural, not medical.

These issues seem to underpin many of the common features of both accidents and poor performance in railways, suburban and metros alike.

If I was starting again, I would adopt this approach.

To embrace the need for analysis requires an appreciation of the repeat patterns of failures and, as a consequence the predictability of common cause 'loss of control' events.

The competence and confidence to apply valid analysis is a skill which needs to be developed by high quality, usable training and reinforced by senior managers seeking information based on valid analysis. This too, presents a challenge since many senior managers lack the basic skill or experience to work in such a way, relying on intuition, or guessing as found in Queensland's Strachan report in 2017.

From an attitudinal perspective Lord Cullen's finding from Piper Alpha that any loss of control event is evidence of management failure is very important and would appear to present a big challenge to many O&M managers because it makes accountability very clear

What is emerging here is the need for training to develop capability, which then needs to be brought into the daily work, not forgotten through non application which seems a to be a common disease.

Finally, curiosity is essential. If things do not seem to quite right, then they probably aren't, so keep asking questions and undertaking in-field observations to test what others are saying in meetings. Without analysis, field observations often reveal that what is being said is wrong.

CHAPTER ELEVEN

Identification of Risks

*F*ollowing the demonstration of understanding of performance and/or condition in my later years I sought that O&M Managers document risks hoping to see a changed profile looking in the short, medium and long term.

The benefit of having a documented list is that its development and status is likely to have been developed collaboratively and shared within a Departmental team, reflecting a mixture of different insights and experiences. It reduces the likelihood of personality dependence, a serious organisational hazard.

Career observations in my early years

We didn't talk about risks in British Rail, only about compliance until late in the 1980s and early 1990s. It was not as if the things were unsafe in British Rail just that we didn't have that sense of 'having to demonstrate that we were taking all reasonable steps' as per the 1974 Health and Safety Act even though the legislation had been passed 16 years before the Clapham accident in December 1988.

After the four multi-fatality accidents in the UK, Zeebrugge, March 1987, Kings Cross, November 1987, Piper Alpha, July 1988 and Clapham, December 1988, in 20 months between March 1987 and December 1988 the realisation that management required systems emerged, not only in respect to safety but other aspects of our responsibilities too.

In British Rail in the early 1990s a series of Board driven Safety Management Initiatives were launched. All good stuff but still with a compliance emphasis. Do this and do that.

At the same time, as I came to terms with the realisation that supervisors ran the railway and that they had deep insights into where problems lay, a new realisation emerged. That O&M Management required a multi-faceted, multi layered, system-based approach.

The new PDSA meeting structure developed in Operations in ScotRail brought that to life ensuring that all areas of risk and performance were considered on a regular basis. What stayed with me from those years is that the mission deliverers, supervisors and front-line managers were both interested and capable of identifying risks and developing very effective, but perhaps not very sophisticated, mitigation measures.

The Alcohol Initiative in Swansea 1990

It was this philosophy that led to the Alcohol Initiative in Swansea in 1990. We had had several cases of dismissing staff for drinking on duty prompting Denzil Lewis a local National Union of Railwaymen (NUR) representative coming to say that we had many staff members with alcohol problems and wanting us to deal with this proactively and in partnership.

Together we visited a charity, Alcohol Concern who arranged for three seminars to be given for our so called 'family groups' of union reps, supervisors and managers. The families were InterCity, Freight and Regional Railways. We all learned together.

What emerged was that South West Wales was a gold medal winner in terms of alcohol consumption in the UK where the average adult male population had approximately 20% of alcohol dependence. If the Rail staff were only half the regional average that meant that 75 staff were alcohol dependent and perhaps 25 train drivers. Wow.

The question for us (Unions and Managers) was how to 'take all reasonable steps' to reduce the risks to ALARP. They knew the names of the people.

What we promised was that any staff member who came forward, even those caught drinking on duty would be redeployed in roles away from front line operations, would enter a scheme managed by Alcohol Concern and that while they were on the programme, they would receive their average earnings from the previous 12 months, rather than only on basic pay which for most families would have represented a stiff financial penalty.

There were some notable successes with rehabilitation, despite some HR protests about setting precedents, at a time when BR did not have a clear policy on this. We acted within my delegated authority. The managers, staff and union reps loved it. At our core, many of our interests were the same.

We took our responsibilities to an otherwise known but unmentionable risk in a transparent and serious way. This is an example of doing what is possible. I have taken this approach into all subsequent roles. Do not be scared to act bravely.

Hazard Logs

I first came across Hazard Logs in 2001 when I joined SBS Transit as part of the team to handle the startup of O&M of two driverless Transit Systems, the North East Mass Transit Line (NEL) and the Sengkang- Punggol Light Rail System (SPLRT) which was a feeder to NEL.

The Hazard Log calculated both the likelihood and potential consequence of risks and scored them before breaking the scores into 4 categories, A to D. Categories A and B had to be closed by design in the project stage and Category C by Procedure by the O&M Team with Category D being deemed to be so low as being acceptable.

This sophisticated methodology was very sound and the discipline and transparency of the risk mitigation measures gave a good reason to believe that the 'taken all reasonable steps' test had been passed.

What this methodology does not deal with very well are the 33 risks which sit within the management of the four key areas of O&M Management; Asset Management, Rules and Procedures, Competence and Modification Control to ensure interfaces remain healthy and tight which is covered in depth in Part Five.

The Hazard Log approach would probably not have led to the alcohol problem in Swansea being addressed, nor would did it help to identify many of the risks which, when addresses saw a significant improvement in reliability in ScotRail, Melbourne or Singapore.

Career observations in my senior management years (Good Practice)

Without a valid and sound basis for demonstrating an understanding of performance and asset condition, risk identification is often unsystematic and incomplete allowing personality dependence and often 'heroic dependence' where a key personality dominates discussion and assessments with a view of 'never mind all that stuff, just do what I say'. It happens a lot, particularly in poor performing organisations.

When O&M Managers have been able to demonstrate a valid understanding of their performance and condition, it follows that they are able to provide a risk assessment based on two aspects:

- Looking back, based on their understanding.
- Looking forward, based on their judgement about future obligations, risks and challenges.

The organisational benefit of this approach is that the senior management are able to test and verify the assessments from Department and Section Heads and supervisors while bringing their own insights and experience into play giving everybody a greater sense of commitment and confidence about the risks and challenges ahead.

I also observed this (Bad Practice)

Almost without exception however, Risk Profiles which do not emerge from either valid analysis of the current state, or a multi-tiered collaboration tend to be full of 'holes' based on intuition (guessing).

<u>At Senior Management Level</u>

A Department Head in one organisation where I worked, and another where I conducted a review - both of whom had hero complexes - also had the worst rate of unplanned, unwanted, unexpected events in respect of safety, reliability and asset performance.

At a Network Level

Southern Region senior managers in 1985, regarding peak hour reliability. It wasn't only me they offended by refusing to accept the evidence and analysis of repeating train service delays but my colleagues and the team of supervisors and front-line staff who observed the daily patterns and received the angry feedback face to face every day.

At a review meeting at the Waterloo Regional HQ I was told that 'they all knew about me, that I had an attitude problem'. Apparently, when I was on late turn (afternoon/evening shift) 'the only thing that you're interested in is getting the punters home'. It was true but I didn't think it was a problem.

Hot Weather in Melbourne 2009

I was asked by the Victorian Minister for public Transport to conduct an independent review into the performance of the Melbourne Network during a period of extreme heat in January and February 2009.

The Regulator and the Operator had decided to proceed with the normal timetable although they were aware that the system was liable to encounter many bad failures in the conditions. The decision was to "give it our best shot", reminiscent of the Charge of the Light Brigade and the Tennyson poem 'into the valley of death rode the six hundred'.

Over the period of extreme heat, the assets and systems failed in exactly the way that the experienced 'asset experts' had expected.

Why didn't the management and Regulator prepare a plan based on the foreseeable risks? Another own-goal for the industry.

Thameslink, UK, 2018

The Thameslink project involving both longer and more trains through the centre of London was brought into revenue service in May 2018 after several years of major asset renewal and new asset delivery. Here is a summary of what happened.

- The Thameslink 2018 Industry Readiness Board concluded that of the 49 issues relating to the smooth running "all but one was considered to have been dealt with" – one month before the new timetable was introduced. Industry leaders, backed by the Dept of Transport (DoT) believed that the changes were on-course.
- The DoT was advised by the industry in early May that they were ready for the new timetable and 'Rail bosses congratulated themselves "on a job well done" weeks before 20 May.

Thameslink Timetable Results 2018

- Warning signs understood in mid 2016
- Failure was beyond doubt' Dec 2016
- 'The component parts of the system were known not to be ready
- New timetable 21st May 2018
- 65% of trains on time – target of 90%

- So why did they start?

- Not enough new trains
- Insufficient trained drivers
- Infrastructure not yet commissioned
- Too complex a timetable
- Supporting management systems not working

The post disastrous launch review conducted by the Chair of Office of Rail Regulator, Prof Stephen Glaister concluded that:

- There was a failure to plan properly - nobody took charge.
- That the Department for Transport, Network Rail, Train Operators all made mistakes which contributed to the collapse of services.
- Risks were often underestimated or not understood at all because of the nature of the were interdependencies.

Groupthink and hope at their worst.

I came to understand that, as a consequence

There are universal obligations of O&M Managers

That O&M Managers key task is to understand and manage their risk profile whatever the particular field or discipline and whatever the location.

The Business Rhythm and resulting organisational processes and systems is an essential enabler of organisational capability. It is the same for Valid Analysis and Risk Identification. It respects information based on analysis and the various insights and experience that is available inside a team.

'Heroes' often hate systematic analysis and risk identification. It removes the power of the so called expert individual. Rather than focusing on 'heroes', systemic management approaches build confidence, ownership, accountability and satisfaction.

Risk Registers: A help or a hindrance?

In modern times there has been a proliferation of risk experts in the industry creating a complex series of matrices aimed at highlighting problems while also tracking risk 'closure'. So how did the Thameslink debacle happen? How was Crossrail in London apparently only 6 months from opening in 2018?

I have come to prefer homegrown risk registers developed around specific rather than general objectives, developed by managers in discussion with their people, helping them to capture the different insights and experience. They are the ones who need to be alert to the possibility of loss of control, who live with both the challenge and the potential consequences. They should emerge from the Business Rhythm of PDSA, not from a discrete consideration focused only on risk.

Risk registers should act as guides to managers, not as constraints or straightjackets.

The benefits of risk registration

I found that risk registration enables Departmental Managers and Line Managers to be risk focused with low personality dependence. In turn this allows 'experts' to be heard and listened to. The brains can be turned on at the gate.

This approach facilitates organisational review and ownership. It puts senior managers in positions to test and verify analysis and allocation of resources. It increases the contribution of others' insights an experience/expertise. It creates a key part of the six-part harmony compared to the solo of the uninformed and often unqualified CEO.

What risks to include in the register?

The Law is clear. Managers and Organisations are expected to take 'all reasonable steps, to identify and mitigate risks to ALARP or SFAIRP in Australia, whereas good practice requires systematic and proactive approach to risks otherwise the 'just too late' and reactive rather than the 'just in time' and proactive culture emerges.

Depending on the issue, the risk could be related to safety, reliability, asset performance, financial, environmental. There are many people with insights and experience within an organisation. At Business, Departmental, Section and Working level different risks and challenges are sought. They should be recorded at that level and reviewed and verified in what I call the two up principle and monitored. The two-up principle prevents a manager from dismissing inputs from their team that they might not want raised.

Who has to be reasonable? All levels of the organisation. Many of the more granular risks are only properly understood at the front line. The two-up risk review process broadens the organisations understanding and enables more experienced and sometimes skillful people to assist with mitigation measures. It also reduces the likelihood of secrecy and lack of transparency emerging or becoming embedded within an organisation.

Who knows about the risks?

In my experience the supervisors were best informed about the nature of many of the risks and were ultimately going to have to deliver the promise.

Ipswich re electrification and staff at risk behaviour. The supervisors wanted help with both issues.

My Area Manager, Graham Eccles led on electrification operability along with me and the local supervisors (a three-part harmony who influenced the train planners making it four parts – it was a great success) leaving me to decide whether I would take action on long standing behavioral problems such as drinking at work, lateness and informal but obvious sickie rosters.

The inclusion of the supervisors was critical to the success of the operability of the timetable. They were able to identify significant risks of the operability plans and be involved in the agreed solutions which they were going to have to make work. The 1985 timetable involved engine changing on all Norwich – London trains with only 8 minutes in one direction and 12 on the reverse. It was as tight as a drum lid. A great lesson from Graham Eccles.

The long-standing problems included habitual lateness of attendance for work, widespread drinking on duty by staff and well organised sickie rosters in some staff groups. At 24 was I a ducker or a confronter of the long-standing problems? No fun in being a ducker.

Risk Register Timeframes

As a Duty Manager the main focus was looking up to 24 hours ahead with an immediate focus on the next hour. As a Traffic Manager with a small area to monitor and manage, the focus was looking forward a week or so with an outlook up to three months at the most.

As a Head of Operations, the immediate focus looked about three months ahead with an outlook up to three years. As a Business MD and CEO the immediate focus was a year with an outlook of 3 to 5 years. It was only later, after seeing how Singapore planned and worked that I came to see the importance of looking beyond 10 to 15 years.

Within a Franchised environment this highlights the importance of the Partnership. The O&M Contractor provides their analysis of performance, condition and risk with options regarding how the risks should be mitigated. Within their contract term the O&M Contractor should manage their risks but longer term, often more strategic risks need to be managed by the Owner, either by shaping the requirements for the next Franchise or for directing the current Contractor to implement a long-term asset and risk pathway.

At these different levels the insights and experiences are all important. High performing organisations are seeking to avoid the foreseeable 'loss of control' events but also the unintended consequences of more strategic decisions which requires that longer term context.

In the short to medium term many of the tactical risks can be mitigated by supporting those close to the front line with senior managers testing and verifying the analysis, risks and challenges identified and their preferred mitigation measures but the senior managers job is also to shape and steer the strategic pathway.

The Risk Register as an indicator of the Culture and Appetite

Experience shows that managers in compliance mode, Administrators rather than Leaders, a focus of Part Four, and administrative cultures prefer to focus on the short-term tactical risks and initiatives rather than the strategic. The tactical focus can give the indication of being busy and focused while the high performing managers and organisations are mainly focused on the long-term strategic risks and challenges where, if successfully managed, are game changers.

'Administrators' tend to leave the more strategic issues in the 'too hard' basket.

I observed one organisation in the last decade who listed 22 actions to address safety and reliability performance challenges. A review identified that when those 22 actions had been completed the underlying performance would be unchanged.

It became clear that there were five known 'too hard basket' issues which had been apparent for some months, which if addressed would fundamentally shift performance. The CEO of that organisation promoted the shift to the 5 strategic issues which within 12 months, led to a major improvement in performance in many areas including reliability – the organisation understood that the senior management team meant business. Meanwhile, most of the 22 tactical issues were resolved by middle and junior managers and their people.

As Tom Peters said, 'high performance is a choice', so is low performance.

I later read this which reinforced my thinking and practice

Piper Alpha

As Lord Cullen expressed in the Piper Alpha Inquiry there were great advantages to what he called home-grown risk control measures. This strongly resonated with my instincts then and still does today, not only with safety but with reliability and asset management too. They included the following:

- By and large, safety has to be organized by the line, those who are directly affected by the implications of failure.
- These people are in the best position to determine the detailed measures necessary
- In fact, prescriptive regulation or over-detailed guidance may at times result in the overall objective actually being compromised.
- If compliance becomes the overriding objective, sight is lost of the more realistic and overall intent that all reasonable steps should be taken.

I completely agree with this, not only regarding safety but reliability and asset management too.

Habits

In the book The Power of Habit by Charles Duhigg the relationship between the commitment and delivery of plans compared to not writing the plans down was explored in a study old people's recovery from hip replacements in Glasgow.

What he found was that in writing down plans people somehow commit to taking that action. By contrast people who do not write down their plans are much less likely to take the required actions. This is not really surprising. When we are busy, we often write lists to help us.

What Duhigg did find in respect to the subliminal impact of writing down plans was that the old people who wrote down weekly exercise action plans following hip replacement were on average walking unaided three times faster than those who did not write down their action plans or record their actions against their plans. He concluded that the process of creating the plans had a significant positive impact on the successful completion of the intent.

In SBS Transit the writing down of the Departmental Asset Management and Operational Plans, their structure, the process of their creation helped to create a sense of commitment to their delivery.

Having to include many people from each Department, their review and validation created a shared, transparent, multi-faceted, highly owned, risk base integrated management plan to deliver the mission.

If I was starting again, I would adopt this approach.

There are two thrusts which emerge here. One relates to bringing the legal obligations to life while the second is about how to create a new organisational mindset about how to bring these obligations to life.

Bringing the legal obligation to life

Firstly, the Plans ensured that managers at different levels were very clear that they had to be able to demonstrate that their risk register reflected their assessment of conditions, practices and performance. This needed to follow on from a demonstration of understanding of performance to give the risks a context. With this they were at first base.

Secondly, the Plans provided a basis for communicating, both explaining and listening, with their people. Consequently, many would take more care when required, or through their own ideas and experiences, would be able to contribute to the risk mitigation.

In SBS Transit after 2016 if there was a loss of control event, I always checked the cause against the Department Management Plan. Had they listed the risk? If they had but they had not yet finished implementing the plan no problem but if it was a new risk, missed off their register then the question was different. How was this risk missed?

How to change the organisational mindset and approach

Sending middle managers for training is often seen as the cure for organisational mindset but without the senior manager's active understanding and support the newly aware and trained middle managers can find themselves in a frustrating position where their new skill is stunted by their bosses continuing to work in the same old ways.

British Rail embarked on a Quality 500 programme in 1989 after the top 50 Directors had been through their own programme. Leadership 500 was followed by Leadership 5000. It certainly helped to release a significant amount of latent capacity and energy in British Rail in the early 1990s but it was still a long way from front line supervisors.

My experience in Swansea with our Alcohol initiative provides another template, one which I would use much more if I was starting out. The secret here was that we took 'family groups' of people together (senior Managers, Line managers, Supervisors and the related Union Reps together from each Business Sector). Each team learned together and committed to handle a major challenge together. It was not top down and secretive.

The most memorable outcomes were those related to a shared determination to do something significant in a very important area of risk, not only to the daily operational tasks, but to the lives of many people. It was powerfully team bonding in a way I had not expected.

Similarly, the approach to training in analysis by Dr Jackie Graham in Melbourne between 1995 and 1997 was done using existing teams and management structures from Senior Managers to Line Managers and Supervisors, natural 'family groups', to address significant cross functional performance challenges. The results were incredible not only in the measurable outcomes but the energy and commitment it inspired.

So, I would train managers and supervisors about their legal obligations in family groups and help them to gain new skills, understanding, competence and confidence to apply their skills.

Chapter Twelve

Resourced risk mitigation plans

*A*fter the need to understand performance and condition, and having identified the risks, this is the easy bit.

It is important to have a mitigation plan which is resourced, along with a schedule for implementation.

Along with the steps regarding performance and risk identification it provides confidence that the O&M Manager is well placed in the discharging of their responsibilities.

Career observations

In SBS Transit Rail in 2016, having spent a great deal of effort in improving our understanding of the patterns of failure enabling the Engineering Discipline Heads to develop their risk profiles and action plans, three categories of action emerged in each Asset class.

Each had a different timeframe and cost consequence. The three categories were:

- A change to the scope and/or frequency of the Planned Maintenance (PM) schedule.
  - o Relatively cheap and often with a significant improvement in the underlying failure patterns.
  - o A surprising consequential benefit was that the 'noise' reduction that occurred as performance and condition

stabilized other otherwise unknown problem areas revealed themselves.

- A changeout of a component.
    - o This often resulted in a step change in a sub system performance and although it required an injection of funding it enabled the System to achieve a more stable, higher performance normal.
    - o As with the change in the PM schedule the step change often delivered immediate and significant improvements in performance, often revealling new issues that were previously hidden within the unreliability 'noise' for the management to work through. The cycle of improvement was not only restarted but with the excitement and confidence of what had already been achieved.
- A redesign of a component or sub system
    - o Of the three steps this is often the most expensive and takes the longest time to implement.
    - o While there are examples of this being the key pathway to improve reliability, predictability and condition of an Asset or sub system, it is not the one where most of the secrets have been unearthed.

What has been experienced in Met Trains in Melbourne in the mid-1990s, in Bukit Panjang LRT (BPLRT) in the late 2010s is that the need for a major engineering redesign to obtain any sustainable improvement was shown to be wrong. In both cases the application of valid applied statistical analysis at sub system level revealed that there was plenty of low hanging fruit.

For Operations, the analysis of Group or Sector performance reveals that they often have quite different System characteristics, as do sub systems of different train fleets for example. As discovered in BPLRT with their assets, and with the improvement in the affected Sectors in Melbourne with the Sector timetable redesigns between 2010 and 2013 the opportunity to achieve a step change is almost always there.

When it comes to the redesign of a Sector or Group timetable it needs to be designed around the point of most constraint, often close to city centers of termini. These inside out designs enable the trains to flow smoothly at their critical points. If the timetables are designed outside in there is usually plenty of conflict and consequential turbulence close to the critical point which results in plenty of late running, particularly when the system is at its heaviest load in peak periods.

In each case the common component was the understanding of the as-is system characteristics; the identification of the risks and challenges informing a resourced action plan.

I have also experienced organisations who reject what the applied statistical analysis reveals, preferring to remain captured by what Strachan referred to as intuition, or I prefer to call guessing. Unfortunately, all those organisations deprive themselves, their customers and their stakeholders and owners of the benefits available from disciplined analysis, disciplined thought and disciplined action.

The power of Harmonies Melbourne 1996

- It was a team job, from top to bottom where many insights and experience were blended together
- Even the old Union reps were thrilled
- The article was posted far and wide by the staff themselves.
- It was a breakthrough as Met Trains went from being unreliable to the most reliable in the country by 2001.
- The power of analysis and disciplined action

AUSTRALIAN QUALITY AWARDS

Competence and confidence on track

When the multi-layered harmonies formed by the multi-layers of an organisation were engaged the success rate is almost always 100% with results often exceeding the most optimistic expectations.

- Met Trains being recognised by the Australian Quality Awards process in 1996.
- The successful development and delivery of the 2000 Sydney Olympic Rail task

- The transformation of SBS Transit reliability after 2015, from mid Premier League to Champions.
- The incredible reversal of the Bukit Panjang LRT reliability after 2017

When those harmonies are not in place, where a valid understanding of the problem is missing, the outcomes generally disappoint all stakeholders' expectations.

I came to understand

That management actions need to be based on analysis and organisational engagement.

If I was starting again, I would adopt this approach.

In a sense this obligation is the easy bit but it needs to be facilitated by the CEO and the Board who might need to commit more resources than they were expecting to do as the O&M organisation goes through a transition. Unfortunately, there are many examples where Boards, particularly in franchised O&M Operators have been shown to be lacking in this respect showing that profits are the number one priority with everything else a long way behind, in line with Board's legal obligations to act in accordance with the interests of their shareholders.

As stated in the earlier sections the managers need to be trained in how to conduct valid analysis to enable them to demonstrate that they understand the performance characteristics of their Asset class and Systems.

They also need to understand the importance of identifying risks and challenges across various timeframes and to ensure that there are resourced plans to modify the systemic characteristics.

While 'Special Cause' events deserve specific action too the quietly, repeating, unsensational, systemic, common cause events hold the key to sustained and step changes in performance.

Action based on intuition, or guessing, has been shown to be ineffective in almost all cases if different outcomes are desired. As Einstein said, "doing the same thing over and over and expecting different results is insanity". Lots of O&M organisations seem to work like this.

CHAPTER THIRTEEN

Investigation of loss of control events

Investigations is another legal obligation on O&M Managers although for some reason it is usually only reviewed and tracked in respect to safety matters.

At the start of my career the clear objective of investigations was to attribute blame to an individual but progressively the industry looked at incidents in a more systemic way.

By the end of my career, I had become convinced that the only real reason for conducting an investigation was to learn about what had gone wrong and to take actions to prevent recurrence.

While the industry makes such statements regarding safety incidents it is obvious from the repeating poor reliability that it is not applied to many other aspects of the Business Operations.

My research between 2017 and 2020 showed that less than 5% of Rail O&M Managers have been trained on how to conduct an investigation. If so few managers are trained in such an important area how can they be expected to identify all the contributing factors and put in place plans to prevent their recurrence?

Career observations

The objective in British Rail in the 1980s and early 1990s was to find a front-line worker to blame, discipline them before closing the file.

The idea that management were responsible for loss control events never entered my consciousness until I read the Piper Alpha investigation! This was despite the UK's 1974 Health and Safety at Work Act requiring managers to have systems in place to ensure that they were providing a safe system of work. I only joined British Rail in 1982, 8 years after that legislation. No training was given regarding this obligation until the early 1990s but the expectation that a front-line worker should be blamed rather than the processes, systems and culture that had entrapped them, was still very much the norm up to when I left British Rail in 1994 to take up a position in Melbourne, Australia.

Newton Train Crash, Scotland, 1991

The Newton train crash Public Inquiry in 1991 had a significant effect on how I saw my responsibilities particularly the examination of the signalman's training and assessment records.

- The signalman did not contribute to the accident in any way but even though he had a high record of assessment scores, typically over 90%, the incorrect answers were always in the same area. How many times does he have to tell you that he doesn't understand an area of competence before you do something about it? Asked by the ASLEF QC. It was a reasonable question, but it wasn't how we thought about our obligations.
- The recently reconstructed junction introduced single lead junctions in June 1991. The driver's error in passing M145 signal at red would not have resulted in a collision on the old layout.
- Key Findings
  - Following a similar collision at Belgrove in Glasgow in 1989 on another single line junction the Procurator Fiscal (Coroner) recommended no more such junctions

should be built. Newton Junction was remodelled with a single line junction in 1991.

- British Rail experts argued that a red signal is a red signal and that the Procurator Fiscal didn't understand that, and railways in general.
- One of the drivers who died at Newton was from the same depot as the drivers for Belgrove. They were very angry.
- Had British Rail taken all reasonable steps? Clearly not. It was a time of soul searching and discussion about the traditional approach. Nobody was held to account.

It was time to test the old chestnuts. The previously accepted 'truths'.

Investigation Reports

In Operations in ScotRail we established formal acceptance of all investigations when we realised that many local inquiries and some senior management-led ones had made many recommendations which had been rejected by senior management, for some reason, and not actioned on.

We implemented a regime where all investigations at any level were based on a written remit or terms of reference. The remit or terms of reference had to be approved two up from the panel chair to ensure that the scope was sufficiently defined.

The remit generally asked for four things but could also highlight specific questions that it wanted the panel to investigate.

- The primary cause based on the events of the day.
- The secondary issues which created the circumstances of the day
- Any interim mitigation measures for implementation before the final report
- A final report and recommendations to prevent a recurrence.

What emerged was a frequent debate at the senior management investigation review meetings where the findings were subject to discussion and approval. We introduced a process where approved or accepted recommendations became part of an action list while findings or recommendations that had not been approved were returned to the panel for further consideration in case the senior review had not understood the underlying thinking. It certainly created a lot of debate about what how we should be addressing issues raised.

Two key learnings for me were the importance of the substitution test. Firstly, did the person on duty who made an error do what their colleagues would have done? This was what we came to call an individual accident or a systemic problem and secondly, the issue of risk. Newton established that not all red signals were the same. Their being passed at red had quite a range of different consequences and so therefore had different risks. The old stalwarts were uncomfortable about moving away from the time-honoured belief that a red signal is a red signal.

Rosanna, Melbourne 1996

Two young boys, under 10, had walked around the back of an up direction train which was waiting for a down direction train to come through a single line section. They walked into the face of the down direction train. The traditional view was that they were, unfortunately responsible for their death since they had effectively trespassed by crossing the railway at an unauthorised point very close to a level crossing. A site visit revealed that the boys had used a well-worn path an crossing point. What they had done had been done by many others.

As with the discussion in ScotRail about the 'opening of a can of worms' when we started to view each signal as having a different level of risk, it was similar here. There was nothing we could do about informal level crossing points otherwise the 'can' would be opened up.

We studied every established unauthorised crossing point and took different measures depending on their risk based on sighting time – at some we established proper crossings, some fencing, some signage. We tried to 'take all reasonable steps'. As with the signal rating in ScotRail, we adopted a better-informed way of thinking about our obligations.

Concord West, Sydney, 1998

This accident occurred in the start up period in the early morning. An empty train was moving south towards the city when the driver received a restrictive signal aspect. He assumed that he was catching up a stopping passenger train. Unfortunately, he wasn't.

The train had been signalled into a passing loop which had a turnout speed of 15 km per hour but had just been reinstated after being locked out for a couple of years. As the train was diverted off the main line at approximately 80 km per hour it rolled over.

The investigation concluded that the driver was at fault. As the CEO of the Train Operating Company, the State Rail Authority, I rejected the finding on the basis that the driver was very experienced, had a good reputation and history. The driver had been trapped.

For several hundred trips the signal had been interpreted in one way but on this occasion, it was meant to be interpreted differently. That the weekly notice included a reference to the loop having been reinstated is not a reliable way of telling people of a significant change in their environment. Had he read it? Had he understood it? Nobody had to ensure either of those two things.

The investigating panel challenged me by saying 'if we move away from a restrictive signal is a restrictive signal', and that the driver should have assumed that this could well have been the one in a thousandth time, then where does it end'? Very similar to the treatment of red signals in Scotland and the unauthorised public crossing points in Melbourne.

This was another case of refusing the look beyond the set-in-stone way of things, quite like reliability in so many cities too.

Following the Newton accident, a series of adjustments were made to the operations of the signalling through Newton Junction before the single lead junction was removed. The Health and Safety Executive imposed a condition on ScotRail's operations management during each change; that every driver who would work through the junction would need to have a face-to-face briefing on the changes in the working arrangements at the start of the particular shift. This was an enormous challenge, thought to be impossible until we established a way of doing it, something that was repeated several times in three years.

Later, while in SBS Transit Rail we created a risk-based regime for ensuring that all affected staff would be briefed on any significant change in any Procedure before the change came into effect. Unlike in ScotRail the requirement was not imposed on SBS Transit. The briefing of the reintroduction of the loop at Concorde West would probably have increased the driver's awareness of the track and signalling arrangements and the accident would probably have been avoided.

Leaves on the Line – a story of industry failure

In the early 1980s, on London's Anglia region the old clasp brake EMUs were being replaced by new disk braked trains.

Despite their improved braking in most conditions, it became well known that when the coefficient of friction between the train wheel and track became compromised the brake became unreliable. It could be mist, dew or leaf debris.

Despite the emerging problem, trains with these brakes continued to be introduced across the industry in the UK. The associated problems included trains quite frequently losing detection and becoming invisible to the signalling system and terrifyingly, trains sliding, in some instances over 1.5km, with the driver having no control during what became known as the leaf fall season – hardly a new climatic condition in the UK.

The general response was that the risk got transferred to the operations people and the civil engineer who began to clear vegetation – not really qualifying as a technical solution even though it had a technical cause.

Leaving aside the problems of transferring the risk control from the Mechanical and Electrical Engineers to the Civil Engineers and the operators, here we are 40 years later after the Salisbury 2021 collision and the primary cause is the failure of disc brakes to operate properly in compromise rail adhesion conditions. This is despite the often heralded 'safety is our top priority' mantra.

How is it that a technical solution has not been found and deployed? After 40 years. In an industry who has been claiming that safety is its top priority for decades!

Investigations are often seen as a task to be completed to comply with a Company Policy or Procedure

They persistently seem to attribute blame, rather than learn or prevent with a tendency only to focus on Special Cause Events. See Concorde West above. It once again demonstrates the lack of understanding or analysis of common cause, systemic events and patterns, highlights the reactive, administrative nature of many investigations.

Some investigations findings are flawed

It is not uncommon that action plans are determined before investigations. This knee jerk approach fits into what Strachan observed in Queensland with guessing and intuition being the key approach to risk management. It excludes organisational insights and ownership from coming to the fore. The experts turn their brains off at the gate and it actively discourages curiosity or investigation and reduces 'experts' to implementing solutions that they know to be flawed. Two examples are listed below:

> • Change the Relays
> Following a major delay, a CEO decided even before the preliminary investigation had been conducted that all the electrical input relays needed to be replaced even when the investigation showed that the cause was the relay settings, not the relays themselves. The predetermined decision to change all the relays went ahead.

> • Stop the testing of the new trains
>
> Another CEO, after an overhead line had been burnt through, without any preliminary data, announced that a new train under test had caused the problem and promptly stopped further testing for 10 weeks.
>
> Meanwhile within 24 hours the preliminary investigation revealed that a local design weakness in the overhead line system at that specific location had led to the breakage. The ban on testing remained in place for ten weeks.

Many investigations findings are ignored

In Studies of 11 Rail O&M Companies, looking at the effectiveness of reliability investigations between 2009 and 2019 frequently found the following:

- That investigations were deemed as being complete without any recommended preventative action plans.
- That previous investigations' findings for similar events had not been followed up.
- That the dominance of top-down action plan made any bottom-up recommended action plans unwelcome, even when the correct mitigation plan was well known.

Zeebrugge, March 1987

193 died

- 'The disease of sloppiness'
- 'At first sight the faults which led to the disaster were the errors of front line staff and supervisors but a full investigation led inexorably to the conclusion that the underlying faults lay higher up in the company.'
- Five near misses with the same cause in 5 years
- Requested investment by Captains to see the bow doors turned down.
- No Laid down systems of work

I came to understand that, as a consequence

Investigations provide a wonderful opportunity to organisations.

> To gain a much better understanding of what is not working properly and to identify areas where improvements can be made to prevent recurrence although the traditional approach of investigations was to find someone to blame. The implementation of the accepted recommendations to prevent recurrence and to strengthen organisational defences is in line with legal obligations recognising that managers are obliged to take follow up action after investigations have been completed and recommendations made and accepted.

Unfortunately, there is a great deal of evidence that this is not done well. Zeebrugge and Kings Cross Fire, both in 1987 provide high profile safety examples. In both accidents middle managers had identified the risks and frequently made recommendations that had been ignored by senior management.

Similarly, the NASA Challenger, 1986, and Columbia, 1993 explosions were both caused by well known weaknesses which middle managers had frequently warned senior managers of their concerns only to be overridden. Diane Vaughan referred to this as the normalisation of deviance, which is discussed in Part Three, chapter sixteen.

Reviews into poor reliability often reveal the same characteristics.

When investigations focus on identifying where the management designed control measures have not been effective and then strengthen them the consequences of an investigation mean that it is unlikely that a recurrence will occur. That is what the Health and Safety legislation requires; for managers to be proactive and to take all reasonable steps to prevent a loss of control event, to learn and act.

What Reason helped to bring out in his book Managing Risks of Organisational Accidents, and is dealt with in the next section, is that it is the same organisation defense weaknesses that lead to accidents and delays. Their causation is the same. Management have not got effective controls in place to prevent loss of control events.

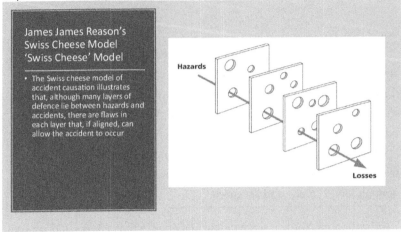

If one accepts the theory that loss of control events are caused by weak or unhealthy organisational defence barriers then it is possible, using outcomes of investigations into loss of control events, to create a frequency profile of weak or unhealthy risk control barriers which have resulted in loss of control.

An analysis of frequency of specific defence failures, such as the one shown here, provides a basis of organisational Risk Improvement Plans.

These can then be used to address the most frequent risk control failures whether the loss of control events are safety, reliability, asset management, emergency readiness, competence assurance readiness etc. This approach can enable organisations to proactively and systematically strengthen the health of their risk control arrangements.

There is a great deal of evidence that this is not done well. Zeebrugge 1987, Kings Cross Fire 1987 and NASA 1986 and 2003 provide high profile safety examples. In both accidents middle Managers had identified the risks and frequently made recommendations that had been ignored by senior management.

In British Rail's Southern Region in the 1980s, ScotRail and Melbourne in the 1990s, and SBS Transit Rail in 2015 it was the failure to understand the systems performance characteristics, a lack of analysis and understanding, that prevented sustainable improvement plans from being developed and implemented. The failures to understand and the associated 'learned helplessness' prevented managers from preventing loss of control events. In this case, repeating causes of delays.

Singapore Reliability: Picking the low hanging fruit

In SBS Transit Rail, in hindsight, the opportunity to achieve an MKBF over 1 million had been present for several years before 2015 as it had on SMRT's Circle Line, where the MKBF reflects the average number of train km operated between delays over 5 minutes.

Similarly, on SBS Transit's SPLRT and SMRT's BPLRT where the underlying reliability over 5 years before 2016 had been an MKBF of 70k and 35k respectively but by 2021 had risen to 350k and 250k respectively.

In the same way, between 2000 and 2003 Melbourne's peak hour reliability was over 95% in both peaks. Why has that been allowed to slip away from being repeated? Even the all-day has remained well below that level. Singapore in reverse?

The point being reinforced here is that, with applied statistical analysis, if a manager has not been trained in how to conduct an investigation it is likely that investigator or the reader's conclusions will be incomplete and probably invalid. If investigations are not conducted to identify and implement measures to prevent recurrence, then where is the learning and the improvement?

The condition of 'Learned Helplessness' is often entrenched by a 'Groupthink'.

This condition prevents or absorbs is used by many O&M managers from taking responsibility for uncontrolled, unwanted, unexpected 'loss of control' events.

How many times did the red signal, SN109 at Ladbroke Grove to be passed by a driver before the employing senior manager would realise that there was a problem? The signal had been passed at red eight times in the previous 6 years. Where was the duty of care?

If not, is it reasonable that they should have been known? Definitely. Could management have taken preventative actions to prevent the accidents? Yes. Lord Cullen was right. These events were evidence of management failure.

In the case of Ladbroke Grove, the chief executive of Railtrack spoke of 'a seemingly endemic culture of complacency and inaction. People have tended to manage reactively, not proactively. The basic management discipline of 'plan-do-review' is absent the further down the organisation one goes'. The plethora of management committees between Railtrack and the Train Operating Companies failed to act. A bit like the failure to see that Thameslink was not ready in 2018.

Regarding Ladbroke Grove I don't think that the senior management felt an obligation to take steps to reduce the obvious risk which seems curious. I am unsure that even now that after the 2021 Salisbury accident the cause will receive a technical solution. In 2015 it was reported that the UK railways spent £15 felling trees near the railway and cut down 1 million trees per week. Where are the mechanical engineering fraternity?

As with safety, the reliability precursors are almost always well-known by people within the organisation but ignored, either deliberately of through ignorance reflecting a lack of training or a lack of an example of good practice?

The Untrained Industry

If O&M managers are not trained or competent in conducting investigations, then how can they be expected to identify all the contributing factors and put in place action plans to prevent recurrence?

As a consequence, the industry has adopted an approach which is probably not complying with the law in many jurisdictions since they were choosing not to act, not to take all reasonable steps because the managers simply did not know how to do it.

Not taking all reasonable steps results in many of the bad incidents and poor performance highlighted in this book. Arguably it is largely based on a lack of ability and competence which then influences the degree of willingness to act and/or to accept that 'bad things happen and that it is inevitable.'

I later read this which reinforced my thinking and practice

Piper Alpha Investigation, 1988

From Lord Cullen's investigation into the Pipa Alpha accident where 167 people were killed when an oil platform exploded in the North Sea off the coast of UK in 1989. From studying this Report, I took three main points of learning.

Firstly, that any unexpected failure or delay is evidence of a failure of management; a failure to having identified the risk factors or having failed to mitigate those risks.

Secondly, that Senior Management are easily satisfied that things are OK. The Report identified that Senior Management was easily satisfied that all the correct steps were being taken about such matters as Training and Emergency preparedness when this was not the case. The various case studies referenced in this book, and my own experience suggest that this 'being easily satisfied' is a cultural disease that is deeply embedded in many Rail O&M organisations.

Thirdly, that non-compliance with inadequately developed Procedures was deeply embedded. The various case studies reveal that informal methods of work emerge even with high risk control procedures. It also highlights that many Procedures are not sufficiently structured to control the identified risk.

The Two Railway Syndrome

This difference between what is written down and what is being done is what I refer to as 'the two-railway syndrome' which is deeply embedded in many Rail O&M organisations. What does it tell us about the level of owner-ship, the level of curiosity and commitment by Senior Managers to identifying this risk and preventing it from being present?

The previous three key observations are cause for great concern. They tell us that the past performance is not a sufficient predictor of the future and that it is likely that things are not as good as they seem, or as being reported. It highlights the need for continuous vigilance and the need for a skeptical mindset from senior managers that challenges the underlying assumption that 'all is well', that things are as good as being reported, although if the managers are experienced in their field, they will be aware of these cultural attributes and weaknesses.

Nimrod explosion, 2006

The Rail industry has progressed, over the past 40 years from having no safety management systems to having a plethora of documented systems. This case highlights that having such documentation is not a substitute for proactive risk identification and mitigation. The notion of the 'fallacy of safety' was identified in the Inquiry, where documentation is relied upon to satisfy the various interested parties that 'all is well' when the evidence showed that this was not the case and was was staring the RAF in the face.

A Nimrod XV230 exploded while on a reconnaissance flight in Afghanistan during refuelling. 14 people died. Charles Haddon-Cave QC led the Inquiry.

The Nimrod had been flying since 1969.Between 2001 and 2005 a Safety Review was conducted on the Nimrod where the focus was to demonstrate that the Nimrod was safe rather than to assess the risks and the relative con-trol measures in place. The findings of that safety review was called a 'lamen-table job'.

It led to the term the 'Fallacy of Safety' entering the vocabulary where organisations use documents to demonstrate that their safety arrangements were robust and effective rather than focusing on identifying the risks and ensuring that effective mitigation measures are in place.

The Inquiry found that:

- The failure data was available to decision makers but had not been analysed. The worsening data trends had not been analysed over a six year period!
- The frequency of fuel leaks was over 40 times what was assumed in the Safety Case.
- Frequency of leaking fuel tanks in the Safety Case required a frequency of leaks to be improbable, 1 or 2 leaks during the operational life of the fleet yet between 2000 and 2005 there had been 40 fuel leaks per year.

This accident is of interest due to two key lessons.

Firstly, as with other cases, the data highlighting the risk was available and known about but not acted upon.

Secondly, over the past decade, while conducting Business Reviews many cases have been found where the organisational processes did not meet the required accreditation requirements where it had been achieved, with certificates often proudly displayed in corporate documents such as websites, and wall mounted displays.

James Reason's book, Managing Organisational Accidents.

From this book I took five key learning points.

Firstly, the concept of 'defences in depth'. A mixture of barriers, often overlapping and mutually supporting, providing successive barriers which make complex technological systems, such as power plants, aircraft and railways safe from severe outcomes due to single failures whether human or technical. These barriers also underpin the reliability and predictability of performance and are illustrated in the Swiss Cheese model.

Secondly, the difference between active and latent failures, where active failures are due to individual actions while latent failures are organisational in nature, often lying dormant within organisations for many years (the incubation period) and often the unintended consequences of senior management decisions.

Thirdly. the differences between errors and violations where violations are when individual actions were a deliberate breach compared to when an individual has made an error of judgement.

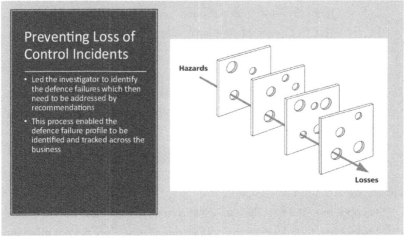

Preventing Loss of Control Incidents

- Led the investigator to identify the defence failures which then need to be addressed by recommendations
- This process enabled the defence failure profile to be identified and tracked across the business

Fourthly, that latent failure are ever present. The Swiss Cheese Model highlights that while the defensive barriers would always be intact in the real world each barrier has weaknesses and gaps, potential 'holes' in the layers of cheese. In the real world the 'holes' come and go, shrink and expand in response to O&M managers actions and omissions.

Fifthly, that Safety and Quality Policies and requirements cannot be an add-on, that as well as the need for discipline and organisational alignment they rely on a belief system focusing on avoiding any loss of control events, to be continually searching for risks and implementing control measures that systematically strengthen organisation defenses.

Using the 'benefit of hindsight test', the frequency with which managers use the term 'with hindsight' after a loss of control event, the factors that result in almost all loss of control events, whether accidents or delays, are generally well known, yet frequently Rail O&M managers choose not to act, not to reduce the likelihood of loss to either ALARP or SFAIRP, despite senior management's commitment to safety and/or customer first.

James Reason is seen by many as a leading developer of contemporary risk management thinking in relatively high technical organisations yet my research between 2017 and 2020 found that, while the Swiss Cheese model is well known very few people understand it, particularly the dangers of aligned 'holes' or failures of organisational controls.

I came to understand that, as a consequence

An incompetent O&M Industry? A harsh but sound conclusion.

What is referred to here as the Universal Obligations of O&M management are not generally known and may well be challenged but they are definitely not taught which is a primary motivation for writing this book.

The absence of compliance with these six universal obligations suggests that the level of professional competence of the various Senior Management teams and their subordinates is very poor.

The investigation into the Kings Cross disaster also included

- The staff forgot that there was a sprinkler system that could have put the fire out.
- Nobody was trained or authorised to operate the firefighting equipment.
- Inadequate numbers to implement required controls in an emergency.

It's a cultural problem at Industry Leader level. Safety, Operational and Asset performance reflects organisations cultures, the way that they do things, their Business Processes and Systems which are, almost without exception very poorly developed. It is common to find that the culture is dominated by personalities and intuition or guessing. This is normal. Reliance on intuition and hope.

I came to see reliability, safety and environmental risks through the same prism. The proactive, systematic identification and mitigation of risks was the first common feature. The second was that there are always precursor events available for interested eyes on closer scrutiny.

Heidrich

Heidrich developed what has become known as the 'iceberg' theory, where the bad safety outcomes are above the surface, outcomes of unsafe acts and conditions below the surface.

Accidents and delays are consequences of either holes in the cheese lining up, or of a series of minor failures. In respect to both accidents and delays the management need to take preventative action to reduce the likelihood of accidents requiring a focus on 'below the consequence line', to reduce the base of the triangle, reducing unsafe acts and failure or non-compliant conditions.

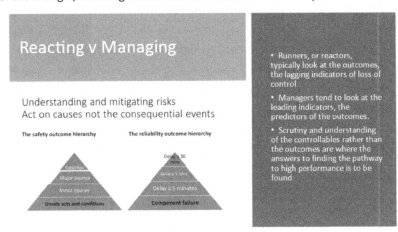

Reliability

As with safety, reliability also requires analysis and action 'below the Heidrich delay line'. Proactive activity is about reducing the likelihood of failure. Delays, above the line, are consequences of failures, not the problem in themselves. Reliability reflects the combined impact of the failure and the quality of the response and/or post failure intervention.

Industry Learning

During my career the Rail Industry becomes very interested in inquiries into major safety incidents. My assessment is that this interest is voyeuristic in nature, not only in Rail but more generally. Why do I write this? The key findings and lessons are often applicable in many sectors but rail O&M Managers seem either ignorant or reluctant, or both, to apply them.

While most Public Inquiries concentrate on major accidents their findings are generally split between the specific technical failures and management/cultural failures. It is quite common for findings to conclude that the source of the loss of control is cultural.

Typical Safety Related Investigation Findings

- Senior Management were easily satisfied that things were fine when they most certainly weren't.
- Informal Systems of Work in place without senior management's knowledge or approval.
- No capability to analyse data, to see the evidence, to understand the problem.
- A refusal to acknowledge the available date.

Clapham, 1988
The Industry challenges emerge

- 'To British Rail the concept of absolute safety was acknowledged and expressed with total sincerity. BR's commitment to safety was unequivocal.'
- 'Bad workmanship, poor supervision and poor management combined to undermine that commitment.'
- 'The appearance to the outsider that things were perfectly safe was not a reality.'
- 'The errors go much wider and higher than merely to remain at the hands of those who were working that day.'
- 'Only by constant vigilance can they seek to ensure that the needless deaths, injuries and mental suffering caused by the accident will not be repeated'
- YAHOO NEWS

The Zeebrugge Inquiry found that 'at first sight the faults which led to the disaster were the errors of front-line staff and supervisors but a full investigation led inexorably to the conclusion that the underlying faults lay higher up

172 • SIMON LANE

in the company'. Very similar to Clapham and investigations into poor reliability of train services.

Typical Reliability Investigations identify the following:

- No valid understanding of performance challenges.
- A refusal to look at data.
- Investigations without any preventative action plans

Unfortunately, Public Inquiries rarely study poor reliability performance.

Poor operational performance on railways is rarely subject to such scrutiny, presumably because the consequences cause significant inconvenience rather than tragic loss of life but the key findings in tragic accidents are almost always the same in both poorly and barely adequately reliable railways.

What became evident in Britain's Southern Region in the mid 1980s, in Melbourne in the late 1990s/early 2000s and Singapore between 2015 and 2021 is that the opportunity to achieve world leading reliability presents itself. When combined with the appropriate ambition, attitude, partnership, skill and discipline, however, outstanding performance followed.

As with the major safety accidents, for poor reliability it is my contention that the precursor signs are always there for interested and curious eyes to see. The managers do not look, or do not know how to look.

If I was starting again, I would adopt this approach.

There are five key areas that I would wish to address.

Firstly, I would want managers to understand the concepts of loss control and to study contemporary safety management theory, such as Reason's Swiss Cheese Model, to understand the need for healthy defense barriers to prevent loss of control events.

Secondly, I would want O&M Managers to understand, as Lord Cullen pointed out, that loss of control events are evidence of management failure albeit whether those failures were about not being aware of the risks or by not acting, or both.

Thirdly, I would ensure that O&M Managers were trained on how to conduct investigations with an emphasis on identifying where the unhealthy barriers were to enable the action plan to strengthen them, to prevent recurrence, to strengthen the organisation.

Fourthly, I would want safety leaders to develop a profile of common defence failures, whether from safety, reliability, asset management, competence assurance or emergency readiness investigations, audits or assessments to guide the development of organisational risk management improvement plans.

Fifthly, I would want O&M Managers to read, study and have to present and discuss their reflections on Investigations outside their immediate area with the objective of identifying applicable lessons but also to broaden their breadth of understanding. The rotating presentations by Departmental Heads in SBS Transit Rail certainly assisted this but I wish we had had study groups. I have found Rail O&M Managers to have a low knowledge of understanding and/or interest about Investigations outside their areas despite so many Reports being available on-line.

Operational Investigations to improve response – never mind what we did yesterday, how would we deal with the same incident tomorrow?

CHAPTER FOURTEEN

Preventative action plans to prevent recurrence.

*T*his too follows on from the H&SAWA obligations. Having conducted the investigation action is required to ensure the loss of control event does not reoccur.

Career observations

Many investigations seem to treat the event as unique despite the well-established patterns of Loss of Control events particularly with reliability but also with safety related events where known factors of weakness are generally well known.

As a consequence, many investigations' action plans only address what is seen to be the active or primary cause whereas a preventative action plan requires the organisation to consider the effectiveness and deficiencies of its own arrangements.

I came to understand that, as a consequence

Adopting the Lord Cullen mantra that management is responsible for all loss of control events is confronting. It is quite an overwhelming reality when Organisation's don't traditionally consider that to be the case.

It requires a new mindset then the development and implementation of a highly disciplined management system to ensure that 'all reasonable steps are being taken'.

By adopting Lord Cullen's mantra, it follows that the only reason for conducting an investigation is to learn about what defences have failed, which brings Reason's thinking into prominence, so that the subsequent action plans are aimed at preventing a recurrence.

While this might appear to be a Railway disease it multiple case studies show that it is quite common in many sectors of society and industry.

I later read this which reinforced my thinking and practice

It was Reason's Swill Cheese model described in Managing the Risks of Organizational Accidents that brought the multi barrier defense model to life. While the model brings many insights with it the question remained how to embed the underlying principles into the broader management thinking. The answer came with PEEPO, a five dimensional investigation process looking at People, Environment, Equipment, Procedure and Organisational, similar to task, material, environment, personnel, and management, another well-established Incident Cause Analysis Method or Incident Cause Assessment Method (ICAM).

PEEPO Training

In SBST Rail in 2017, when the emphasis on understanding, risk identification and resourced mitigation plans coupled with our well-established Business Rhythm, we embarked on a Management Training initiative to assist us with gaining a more sophisticated approach to investigations with a particular emphasis on trying to embed an approach to investigations to prevent recurrence and to strengthen organisation capability.

We engaged with Dr Graham Edkins, an Australian specialist who had conducted his PhD under James Reason.

He helped us to understand two key things. Firstly, that loss of control events occurred when the holes in the cheese lined up and secondly, that the health of the control barriers needed to be kept high to close any holes and to strengthen the organisational barriers once a weakness had been identified.

It was not an easy step to make. Investigations were to be based on identifying which barriers had been breached for the holes to line up rather than identifying what had happened. His training helped us to focus on the health or absence of barriers.

What was useful was that the process could be applied to any loss of control event; Accidents, delays, failure to properly review Procedures, staff failing emergency readiness assessments etc giving us a broader profile about our weak barriers than only those revealed through safety or reliability loss of control incidents.

In turn this enabled us to start to build a broader profile of weak barriers more generally enabling the Safety Management Plan to become informed by this profile.

It is interesting that in June 2016 most managers in SBS Transit Rail believed that it was impossible to achieve an MKBF of 400k by 2018, and again that an MKBF of 800k was impossible for 2020 yet for NEL and Downtown Line in 2021 an MKBF of 2million and 3 million respectively has been achieved.

If I was starting again, I would adopt this approach.

I would train managers in four specific points:

Firstly, that investigations are opportunities to learn, never to blame unless there is evidence of gross misconduct, about the health of Management designed arrangements (barriers) which are supposed to prevent loss of control events.

Secondly, that Lord Cullen was right when he wrote that 'loss of control events' are evidence of management failure also based on a reflection that these events are almost always foreseeable to the expert eyes.

Thirdly, that investigations and their recommendations should be focused on preventing a recurrence. You need to determine what happened and then you can focus on preventing a non-occurrence.

Fourthly, that keeping all the defense barriers healthy, and knowing their health status requires a high level of discipline and a skeptical mindset recognising that what Lord Cullen found at Piper Alpha, management is easily satisfied that all is well. It is only in the high performing organisations who have an underlying belief that tomorrow will probably be a bad day that that attitude is generally well attuned to this. Administrative organisations accept that bad things will happen because you can't do everything – not a very good starting position.

CHAPTER FIFTEEN

Organisational alignment and engagement

W hile this is not a legal obligation of O&M Managers under the H&SAWA it is a critical accountability of managers. Previously, I have referred to the need for senior managers to enable multi-level leadership and ownership, to release the latent capabilities and ambitions of their people. Unless the Manager understands this and acts on it, preferring to be the traditional 'controller', an organisation is unlikely to achieve and sustain high performance.

Career observations

I have already made several references, particularly in chapter five, to the power of aligning multiple layers of valuable insights and experience into analysis, risk identification, planning and risk mitigation. My experience and practice reflect my belief that experienced supervisors and front-line staff provide a deep well of insights and reflections.

When combined with my belief that at least 95% of people want to do a good job and be part of shaping and delivering a mission of outstanding performance it seems that senior managers have an obligation to enable their people to enjoy the pride and memories that comes on such a journey.

The power of the six-part harmonies is shown by great choirs (usually 4 parts) and orchestras where the sum of the parts is exceeded through the collaboration and cooperation. Nobody or instrument is superior. The outcome is the result of the blend.

In organisations, the six levels are the Board and CEO, the Heads of Engineering, Operations, Safety and HR, the Heads of Discipline, Section Heads within the disciplines, their supervisors and the frontline staff.

One of the challenges for the Leaders at each level is to create an environment where the experts at each level, in each discipline are empowered to turn their brains on at the gate, not off. It is the senior management's role to create the DNA of 'how we all work together here'.

In my experience the opportunity to do something remarkable always presents itself. Are the senior management up to the task?

In Operations in ScotRail in the early 1990s we embarked on an uncertain journey where our Business Rhythm enabled us to look at performance, risks and challenges in a more structured way than before. We challenged ourselves on whether we were really 'taking all reasonable steps' or whether we were assuming that what had been passed to us had been the best we could do. It was a great credit to my senior colleagues who had considerably more experience and knowledge than I had, that they came on the shared journey.

We were able to transform the sense of what was possible in terms of reliability but also in terms of our proactiveness in respect to Operational Safety, particularly in respect of investigations and the approach to issuing operating instructions to signal boxes. Not perfect but much better.

In Melbourne in the mid-1990s the inherited position was similar to ScotRail with two exceptions. That there was an entrenched but incorrect view of the main problems but secondly a greater willingness to embrace a new approach. The senior staff were exhausted from trying to get better results in their time-honoured approach.

The Power of Harmonies
Melbourne 1996

- It was a team job, from top to bottom where many insights and experience were blended together
- Even the old Union reps were thrilled
- The article was posted far and wide by the staff themselves.
- It was a breakthrough as Met Trains went from being unreliable to the most reliable in the country by 2001.
- The power of analysis and disciplined action

It was not only the results that created the career highlight, including the promise to Government of delivering peak hour reliability of 95% by 2000 (achieved), but the sense of pride that emerged, felt by the whole organisation.

For the 2000 Sydney Olympic Rail Task the challenge was quite different. When the senior team created a high-level critical path map in January 1998 showing all the key tasks, we found that by doing everything in the time proven way we would be about 12 months late. The approach to almost every part of the planning had to be done very differently in an organisation that had struggled with change for many years. We had no choice.

By breaking the tasks down into clear chunks, the various disciplines, or combinations of disciplines went away to try to find a way of delivering the required outcomes faster than had ever been possible before. Elsewhere the story of the Rolling Stock team is told of how they went from this is impossible to creating a path where they were confident and committed to delivering 98% fleet utilisation. The timetable development team faced an even more challenging task with so many Test Events and a new network wide timetable being implemented only 5 months before the Olympic Games with the new Airport Line being opened in May 2000.

The number of train drivers required went up by about 20%. A new training and assessment regime was needed and delivered with all those new drivers coming from Guards. Consequently an increased workforce of guards by about 35% was needed to enable the Train Crew programme to be delivered.

The senior team took on the role of reviewing, testing assumptions and, depending on our respective backgrounds, the details too. Who delivered the Task? Many hundreds of people who took up 'leadership' roles in shaping the strategy and the implementation, people who showed an interest and capacity to go much further than the organisation had traditionally allowed.

The Media expectations were low but even they changed their minds. Our most severe critics gave us 95%. These became wonderful career highlights for so many people.

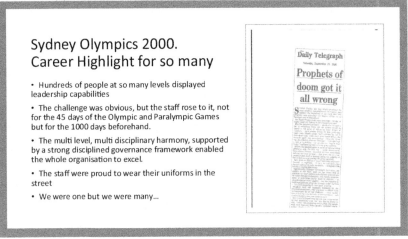

Sydney Olympics 2000. Career Highlight for so many

• Hundreds of people at so many levels displayed leadership capabilities

• The challenge was obvious, but the staff rose to it, not for the 45 days of the Olympic and Paralympic Games but for the 1000 days beforehand.

• The multi level, multi disciplinary harmony, supported by a strong disciplined governance framework enabled the whole organisation to excel.

• The staff were proud to wear their uniforms in the street

• We were one but we were many...

Daily Telegraph
Prophets of doom got it all wrong

The twice-walked journey with SBS Transit Rail also provides a great example of the power of the sum of the multi part harmonies.

In 2003 there had been several other driverless systems introduced elsewhere but always with many breakdowns and failures in the early period. In SBS Transit we had to take over and operate two different driverless Systems in the same year: The North East Line and the Sengkang-Punggol LRT, with less than 20% of staff having any prior rail experience.

We managed to deliver two smooth startups, not without some challenges and hiccups. The Systems were new to all of us making the search for the best approach to many issues a shared journey of exploration gathering different insights and experience. This was true at the senior level but in many disciplines too. We were all learning. The need for a set of Guiding Principles and a structured governance process was important. What we had to do had not been achieved before anywhere.

When asked by the Board what the secret ingredient was, I replied that 'it was the leadership of hundreds of different people in different areas of the organisation and at many levels'. No top down 'do as I say'.

In 2015 the challenge was different. We wanted to test ourselves to see whether it was possible to avoid 38 of the delays over 5 minutes that had occurred over the past two years where there had been prior knowledge of the risk and vulnerability. Time for data analysis and adherence to a more structured governance process.

By 2021 it had become clear. Over the past four years there have been only one or two delays over 5 minutes in each year. The discipline, the analysis, risk identification, mitigation measures and the willingness to buy into a different, more challenging approach to their responsibilities by so many managers and their teams, who succeeded in delivered a so-called 'impossible' outcome. It became the well-earned result of 'having taken all reasonable steps' to reduce the risk to As Low As Reasonably Practicable' - a team of experienced, willing professionals making a truly champion team.

I came to understand that, as a consequence that Rail O&M is primarily a people business rather than technical.

What characterises the highest performing organisations? I have been a long time admirer of MTR in Hong Kong. Their processes and systems are well developed and remain only carefully modified as different post holders have passed through the various key roles over the years. That itself is rare but their ability to raise and sustain outstanding performance over more than 30 years is a testament to their various leaders, their culture, how they do things. They do not, and have not suffered from personality dependence, another key feature of sustained excellence.

When I returned to SBS Transit Rail in 2015 I made it my business to concentrate on creating a set of procedures and management systems that would outlast me, in an attempt to build a culture which was embedded around the seven Foundations of Excellence, described in Part One, the

Universal Obligations of O&M management and the problems of having Untrained Managers as outlined in this Part Two.

A key moment of reflection took me back to MacDonald's, Heidelberg in October 1985 where I realised that the cheeseburger was exactly the same as in London. MacDonald's have processes and systems that are enshrined. They underpin the quality of the product. I have learned that without those established Processes and Systems predictability and sustainability is low.

I later read this which reinforced my thinking and practice

Jim Collins highlighted key features of high performing companies including, each of which resonate with my own experience:

- Companies that transform do not go about motivating their people. They provide them with an environment where they motivate themselves.
- The review processes involved no blame but only improved understanding of the separable parts and the interdependencies.
- There was an absence of celebrity, no heroes, only the mission. Heroes don't like systems and processes, they love chaos.
- The Departmental Management Plans broke down the complexities and reduced them to bite size chunks that enabled insight and deep understanding.
- There were no magical identifiable moments. It came from one more step in a long chain of steps, a victory of steadfast discipline.

If I was starting again, I would adopt this approach.

There are five key issues to be highlighted.

Firstly, that managing and running organisations are quite different.

Secondly, that O&M Managers have universal obligations that enable them to fulfill their Legal obligations:

- To be able to demonstrate that they understand performance
- That they have identified the risks and challenges looking forward.
- That they have a resources mitigation plan.
- That they investigate loss of control events to gain a greater understanding.

- That the consequential action plans are aimed at preventing a recurrence.
- That their people, staff and contractors are competent, aligned and engaged.

Thirdly, that risks and insights on how to identify and resolve vulnerabilities in the O&M environment are to be found at various different levels of an organisation. A key part of the senior management challenge is to gather, reflect and often to act, and be seen to act, on their expertise to help build a single, risk based, integrated management plan. Certainly, this has been a cornerstone in all of my career highlights.

Fourthly, that many people at many levels have a desire and a capability to display leadership behaviour and capacity as part of shaping and implementing a successful mission. Are the senior management capable or interested in creating that environment? The high performing organisations are, in fact they rely on it. They want and need 'all brains turned on at the gate', not turned off because nobody in a more senior position is interested. Create the right environment the people will do all the motivating required in many relatively invisible places.

Fifthly, the Business Rhythm needs to guide and empower the shape of the emerging ideas to avoid chaos.

PART THREE: 'Culture is the game'.

Looking back through my various experiences from different places I found a few distinct cultural differences emerging between low expectations, low performing organisations where there was almost a refusal to look for a better way.

In many organisations the general approach was to go through the motions, where performance was about exceeding the minimum standards and where compliance was the essential driver of expectations.

The most enjoyable, and highest performing was where the will to do as well as could possibly be envisaged was apparent.

Diane Vaughan coined the term the Normalisation of Deviance in her book about NASA's Challenge disaster. She defined it 'the gradual process through which unacceptable practice or standards become acceptable. As the deviant behaviour is repeated without catastrophic results, it becomes the social norm for the organisation.' It seems there is a distinction to be made between the deliberate ignoring of an obvious risk and ignoring a risk or challenge from a lack of know-how. The willingness test.

CHAPTER SIXTEEN

'The Normalisation of Deviance'

Career observations

Despite the earlier sections of this book highlighting challenges around technical and general management competence I found plenty of evidence that Culture is King.

At Ipswich in 1984 a senior project manager said that the service 'will be unreliable for a few months after the start of the newly electrifies services because "it is always like that"'. Why were there such low expectations when all the elements of the development and delivery of the plan were in our hands?

Before that my boss in Broxbourne told me that 'I can't go to London and tell them that the train plan has a flaw in it. They would remove me from my post'. In 1986, whilst a Duty Manager at Victoria Station, the analysis I conducted highlighted both a flawed train plan and repeatedly slack operational execution at some key locations was greeted with anger. Why was there an angry, entrenched reaction to analysis?

In ScotRail and in Melbourne between 1991 and 1997 I found groups of managers who were ambitious and willing to do much better with less stress but had never been trained on how to look.

This was followed by the Sydney Olympic Rail Task and the startup of Singapore's North East Line where the prevailing attitude was to find a way, to harness the insights and experience of many people at different levels in the organisation to exceed the stakeholders' expectations.

In Melbourne in the mid-2010s I observed the Operator giving up the drive to deliver 95% reliability finding that 92% was sufficient. Having given up the ambition performance gradually slid downwards over the following five pre COVID 19 years.

In my final full-time role in Singapore between 2015 and 2017 we challenged ourselves to find a way of never having a delay over 5 minutes. What emerged was a shift from a delay every 3 weeks or so to only one or two per year.

As an Advisor to a young but courageous management team I witnessed the Bukit Panjang LRT system operated by SMRT in Singapore going from being a reliability basket case to high performing.

The second SBS Transit experience in Singapore confirmed in my mind that loss of control events, delays, injuries and accidents, are rarely a surprise to the knowledgeable insiders. The risks were well known.

This is not only confined to O&M but some key areas of engineering research and development too. The problems with poor braking performance with Multiple Units with disc brake trains has been known about since the early 1980s yet despite the frequent claims of 'safety is our top priority' why hasn't a technical solution been found and implemented yet. I write this three months after the 2021 train crash in Salisbury, UK when a disc braked DMU slid unable to brake. Is this the best we as an industry can do?

What happened to the reference in the UK's Health and Safety Executive's 1993 commitment in Ensuring Safety in Britain's Railways that 'the need to ensure that appropriate facilities for safety research and technical evaluation remain available to railway undertakings in Britain should be borne in mind by the Department of Transport when developing proposals for any disposal from the public sector' of the existing BR research and development facilities'. Clearly the industry has failed in its duty.

The 'Fallacy' of ISO 55001 Accreditation

In the Nimrod Inquiry Charles Haddon-Cave QC (2006) into a mid air explosion of a plane during refueling referred to the 'fallacy of safety' in that the UK's RAF had relied on a flawed Safety Case prepared by BAE, its contractor, where the objective was to write a case that showed that the Nimrod was safe even when the data showed it was not.

In recent years I have conducted reviews in several Rail O&M organisations whose senior management were proud of their accreditation only to find that 'the requirements of an ISO 55001 accreditation 'do not apply to us' according to all their Departmental Heads in Engineering although the certificates on the wall made it clear that it did.

In one I found that the Asset Managers of had no understanding of the need to have an Asset Management Plan to meet their ISO 55001 obligations. Reading one Australian O&M Company's Asset Management documentation and I found multiple references to what they were committed to doing in respect of Asset Management - specifically in a UK based Operator – a careless case of cut and paste by the company and presumably also missed by the ISO auditor.

These companies all had significant reliability problems, all had a culture of shallow investigations with no preventative action plans following investigations into significant loss of control events, no valid trend data analysis yet all were apparently committed to safety and customer first priorities.

I came to understand that, as a consequence

That the 'Normalisation of Deviance' is common in respect to risks associated with reliability, competence, safe systems of work, emergency readiness and foreseeable risks. The commitments regarding safety first and customer first seem hollow, and when scrutinised, most O&M company's commitments are indeed found to be hollow.

The precursor signs are almost always staring managers and their teams in the face but there is something that stops them seeing or believing.

Policy Deviance in O&M Companies is also common.

In the last decade or so I have taken a particular interest in reading the different company Policy Statements, often found in waiting areas at reception and in meeting rooms, when I discovered that senior staff in the respective companies were either unaware of their statements or simply ignored their promise. Examples include:

- Being offered a drink in polystyrene cups which are forbidden under the Environmental Policy of that company. When challenged, the CEO of that Company suggested that they change their Policy to make compliance easier.

- Finding that Maintenance Managers in two organisations declared that the requirements of ISO 55001 did not apply to them despite the certificate being on display in the foyer of the HQs and Depots and in the conference rooms.

- Finding references to an O&M Company from another country when reading another's Asset Management Policy documentation after they had been accredited. Nobody had picked up the obvious plagiarism - including the auditors.

Cultural norms within organisations are very powerful.

'The way we do things here', the prevailing culture and the underlying assumptions and practices shape the beliefs about the extent to which 'loss of control events' are inevitable.

They shape the power of what Barry Turner, an American Sociologist referred to as the organisational Incubation period in his book Man Made Disasters (1978), where companies use their long-established approach to risk identification and mitigation, and performance to define themselves: to not see things which are abnormal, to ignore the warning signs that things are not as they should be.

From British Rail in 1984 to Singapore in 2018 recognising and dealing with this blindness has been a constant challenge, the blindness normally driven from the most senior managers in O&M Organisations in conjunction with Regulators and Government Owners, senior bureaucrats.

Lessons from many Major Inquiries, most of which are safety related because poor reliability has not attracted the same level of interest even though the causes appear to be the same. This book attempts to draw out many applicable lessons from Major Inquiries, Rail or not and to highlight that the identified weaknesses reoccur frequently in respect to Rail, particularly reliability.

Typical shortcomings from Safety related Inquiries refer to such things as:

- Senior Management were easily satisfied that things were fine when they most certainly weren't.
- Informal Systems of Work in place without senior management's knowledge or approval.
- No capability to analyse data, to see the evidence, to understand the problem.
- 'It was not the fault of those on duty that day'. The blame lay with senior managers.
- A refusal to ignore the available data.

In the Ladbroke Grove Inquiry in 1999, it came to light that the signal had been passed at danger eight times over six years. When were the responsible management going to notice and act? The QC found that the approach to the identification and mitigation of serious risks was 'slack'.

Railway reliability and safety problems have often been shown to reflect organisational cultures too where the power of the Incubation period, the collective determination not to see or act, or both, reflected itself.

It is my strong opinion that it was a refusal to act that led to the 2021 Salisbury Train crash. The British Rail network management had come to see trains sliding without the driver having any control as normalised in the autumn period. Safety first? I don't think so. A proactive and systematic identification and mitigation of risk? Definitely not.

I later read this which reinforced my thinking and practice

The Normalisation of Deviance: Experience from NASA .

Diane Vaughan concluded that the Shuttle Programme between 1981 to 2003 operated with a culture where significant errors were based on a mindset of conformity to cultural beliefs, organisational rules and norms. She asserted that the normal behaviours reflected NASA's bureaucratic, political and technical culture.

Her findings included that middle managers, the seasoned professionals, couldn't get heard if the message didn't fit. Same as in several notable O&M organisations reviewed between 2018 and 2020 in respect to reliability and asset performance.

She found that in NASA modifications to rectify known areas of risk were routinely turned down. That the Top-Down determination of what should be done prevailed.

She predicted that the Challenger 'loss of control event' would be repeated because nothing had been learnt or changed. Tragically, it did in 2003 when the Columbia broke up on re-entry to the world's atmosphere.

Diane Vaughan wrote that NASA had a culture that 'provided a way of seeing things that was simultaneously a way of not seeing things' - that organisational norms or blindness held organisations back.

The inability to see a better way is due to what? A lack of appetite and curiosity, an untrained incompetence and an easy acceptance that things were as they should be and a refusal to look outside the box to consider learning from others?

What is evident is that this blinkered approach is common not only in Rail O&M but in the Oil exploration and refining and Health sectors. It would appear to be due to senior leadership rather than technical competence.

If I was starting again, I would adopt this approach.

I would emphasise two things:

Firstly, that the job of the O&M Manager is to avoid any loss of control events which requires having a valid basis to understand condition and/or performance, a sophisticated knowledge of the risks and challenges and the need to have a resourced mitigation plan.

Secondly, that any loss of control event should be regarded as their failure.

Together, this should provide a basis of being able to satisfy an interested person or body that you are fulfilling your legal obligation, to systematically and proactively identify and mitigate risks to as low as reasonably practicable, ALARP or so far as is reasonably practicable (SFAIRP).

It's not rocket science, except at NASA perhaps.

CHAPTER SEVENTEEN

Leadership ʋ Process Administration

Career obseruations

One of the challenges is the general acceptance of mediocre performance, where results are accepted as being good enough in an environment where 'Groupthink' and 'Learned Helplessness' are allowed to prevail. This is often characterised with low and broadly shared accountability where no senior manager is to blame when things go wrong. Everybody, O&M Managers and Regulators seem to hold hands and sing kumbaya.

I came to characterise this culture as Administrative where compliance and achieving minimum standards is the focus. Declaring that a new possibility is available as SBS Transit Rail did in Singapore in 2015 is often not welcomed. It represented a breaking of the ranks.

When I was acting as Depot Manager in Battersea in South London, where trains are stabled and cleaned between the morning and evening peak I had a visit from Trevor Toolan, BR's Director of Employee Relations. We walked around the depot and I explained what the scope of work was and how the standard was being improved. At the end he asked me 'are the trains clean now? I explained (again) what we had been doing so he repeated his question. I must have looked a bit confused, so he asked me to stand next to him and look back at the trains as he repeated the question for a third time. I suddenly realised what he was asking so replied that the trains were filthy. He thanked me for my time and bid me good luck and went on his way. What was I going to accept as the standard?

When we were planning to announce a new MKBF target of 500k, up from the two-year standard of 200k my CEO asked me 'what if you fail to achieve 500k?' I replied that although an MKBF of 400k could be seen as a failure it would still represent great progress, so he agreed to us announcing a new MKBF target of 400k. Nobody believed that an MKBF of 400k was possible even though MTR in Hong Kong had been operating at 800k for some years.

In London in 2015 I asked a former senior manager from the City to Coast Trian Operating Company, (the old British Rail London, Tilbury and Southend network) about the possibility of using relay drivers at Fenchurch Street to significantly increase peak hour train frequency without any infrastructure enhancements. He said it was intrinsically too difficult and unreliable even though the Victoria Line had been using this practice for many years and that by 2018 were operating 36 trains per hour off two platform faces at Brixton. How come there was such a reluctance to adopt such a well proven practice from within the same city?

In Melbourne a roadmap was set out to get peak hour reliability back to 95% from 85% in 2010 but the management gave up when they achieved 90% in 2014. In both cases there the accepted norm was relied upon to avoid the risk of perceived failure of doing something perceived as difficult. As Jim Collins wrote in chapter one of Good to Great, 'good is the enemy of the great'. Good is enough.

Looking back what is clear is that high performance came from challenging accepted norms, from find a way of doing what 'going through the motions' defined as impossible. The strange thing about this is that it is the customers, the staff and Authorities all want senior managers to take them on a journey of delivering much better services.

Looking back, the Sydney Olympic Rail Task delivered a fleet utilisation over 98% over a six week period. Met Trains in Melbourne delivered over 95% 'on time' in peak periods for three years when the Jolimont Rationalisation Project was finished in 2000, SBS Transit Rail exceeded an MKBF over 1.5

million for three years from 2018, quite an achievement considering the 400k km 2018 target was regarded as impossible in 2015 and Bukit Panjang LRT, operated by SMRT achieved a 12 month MKBF of 250k in 2021 when in 2017, at the start of the new reliability push the 7 year average MKBF was approximately 30k - deemed as impossible by the holders of the status quo.

Similarly, when Sea Containers took over the East Coast Main Line in the UK the CEO asked why the trains were dirty in the winter. The managers explained that in cold weather the train wash plants do not work. He challenged the team to find a way of keeping the trains very clean even in cold weather. Having been challenged they solved it. In hindsight, not surprisingly the only barrier to providing clean train exteriors in cold weather was the fact that the norm of dirty exteriors of trains was a well-established norm in cold weather.

Tom Peters has been a visionary advocate for excellence since the 1980s and while some of his findings are well known the idea that 'meetings and audits should be stimulators' of the possibility of 'what ifs' being a new and challenging one. It is how I came to see them too, rather than laboriously going through the normal, backward looking, checklist style that many people are familiar with. Two key issues arise from this.

Firstly, that it is possible that meetings can be interesting and fun - where the question about the new possibilities can arise. Secondly, that audits can be a great source of new insights. As a Line Manager my approach to audit was to vigorously defend the effectiveness of our performance, until I came across an intelligent, more pedantic, more rigorous auditor on BR's Western Region, a man called Chris Hogan.

Chris always found weaknesses in the effectiveness of everybody's arrangements. While I found him almost too fastidious, it was impossible to fault him, so I submitted. After that, I welcomed the opportunity that fresh eyes would probe our arrangements and provide an opportunity to learn something. It was a good lesson and has often helped to identify a way forward in an area where we were not in sufficient control of one or more of the underlying risks. It was an important learning step for me.

I came to understand that, as a consequence

That mediocrity is common, that most O&M Managers are satisfied with delivering a 'safe' performance and that high performance is rare.

Looking back, I came to define the 'safe' managers as Process Administrators rather than Leaders. Leaders challenge the norm and very often deliver results previously regarded as impossible.

I later read this which reinforced my thinking and practice

In 2009 Ng Chee Khern, a former Head of Defense in Singapore published an essay which spoke of distinguishing between what he called first and second order thinking.

He wrote that 'First Order' thinkers (Leaders), ask whether 'they are doing the right things' and focus on the ends whereas 'Second Order' thinkers, (Process Administrators), ask whether 'they are doing things right' and focus on the means.

He found that first order thinkers can take the organisation on a new mission whereas second order thinkers will maintain the status quo.

Rail O&M managers tend, more often than not, to be 'second order thinkers, Process Administrators. They are allowed to get away with it. An obvious example was when the UK's CEO of the Rail Delivery Group commented in 2017 when only one Train Operating Company had delivered more than 67% of trains within 5 minutes of being late when he stated that 'our railways perform very well compared to others'. Really?

In George Muir's excellent biography of Bob Reid, the former British Rail Chairman, he repeated the claim that ordinary performance was good, 'that punctuality should be 90% although anything above 85% is adequate, just'. Even when the same trains are late everyday due to the entrenched but invisible blindness to look?

Berkeley University Research Group conducted field research into highly complex, technology intensive organisations that must operate, as far as humanly possible, a failure-free standard. Railways fit this criteria. They found that high performance organisations tend to be preoccupied with the possibility of failure, with expectation of breakdowns and errors and a mindset of intelligent wariness.

Tom Peters, in The Excellence Dividend (2018) highlights his key findings regarding High Performing Companies that define organisations that achieve sustainable excellence. They include:

WITHOUT DELAY • 201

- That excellence requires a state of mind, a belief system, a spiritual belief.
- That excellence is achieved by facing up to the challenge rather than hoping that they will go away.
- That meetings and audits are used to stimulate curiosity about 'what ifs'.
- That people way down the line know what they are supposed to be doing in almost all situations and are trusted particularly if the handful of Guiding Principles are clear.

These features are not well established in Rail O&M companies. A clear picture is beginning to emerge about the difference between the high performing organisations and the rest. I found each of these references very informative.

If I was starting again, I would adopt this approach.

Three key points emerge here.

Firstly, the issue of appetite arises again here. It seems to be very rare that when things go wrong from a reliability, asset management or safety perspective that it is a real surprise to the informed. The Public Inquiries into major accidents in various sectors of industry, and reviews into poor performing Rail O&M companies highlight repeating themes.

As an O&M manager you have to decide whether you are going to be a 'safe' manger or whether you are going to challenge the accepted norms: To be a Process Administrator or a Leader.

Secondly, O&M Managers need to decide whether they want to be first or second order thinkers. Are you wanting to do the right things (first order) or do the things right, to comply with expectations of the status quo, (second order)? There won't be any high performing companies dominated by second order thinkers.

Thirdly, this choice has to be made at many levels so there are no hiding places. If your boss is a second order thinker, it doesn't require you to be the same.

CHAPTER EIGHTEEN

The Question of Senior Management Culpability

In these days of Latent Factors, a culture of low accountability for O&M senior managers and Regulators has emerged which seems to be characterised by low appetite and no or little consequences for loss of control incidents or poor trends despite the relatively large salaries compared to 25 years ago.

This section explores the relationship between performance and the cultural characteristics of three categories of culture – I could have chosen five or ten but three provides fewer hiding places.

Despite the frequent reference to management accountability, when things go wrong, when key individuals have failed to act, either by omission or deliberately, nothing seems to happen to them. This lack of accountability gets covered up even when independent inquiries describe the management approach to issues as slack and complacent.

Having read a number of organisational culture studies I started to consider whether there were common traits which described organisational cultures in Rail O&M organisations.

I studied Ron Westrum's Three Culture Model. He is an American sociologist and has published several papers on his theory. I was persuaded by his three categories which are as follows:

- Pathological/power orientated

- Bureaucratic/risk orientated
- Generative/performance orientated.

After studying a series of safety investigations and characteristics of poor operating performance I gradually refined Westrum's three categories where cultural characteristics and O&M performance come together.

What stimulated the development of this categorisation?

Reason had considered Westrum's three categories in the context of accidents. What I wondered was whether there was evidence of cultural (how we do things here) behaviours that typified poor, mediocre and high performance in a broader context, particularly regarding reliability and asset performance but also in areas of leading indicators such as the approach to investigations, emergency readiness, openness to learning etc.

Since it is rare that the causal factors were not well known whether it be related to safety, reliability, competence, emergency readiness etc the question whether Reason's finding that latent risks are inevitable and ever present allows managers to excuse themselves from blame for the unexpected, unwanted events.

Isn't explaining away poor performance to the inevitable existence of latent conditions a bit too convenient? The question arises whether the decision makers, the managers, knew about the risk that culminated in the 'loss of control' event? If yes, had they taken all reasonable steps to mitigate the risk? If they didn't, should they have?

Certainly, in SBS Transit Rail in mid-2015, when we realised that the causal factors resulting in the vast majority of delays over the previous two years had been well known, there was a sense of collective culpability for not having discharged our professional obligations very well. It acted as a motivator for improvement. Since we knew the causal factors how good would it be if we became proactive rather than reactive?

Looking back through my career, when considering loss of control in respect to safety, reliability, asset condition, competence, emergency readiness I find that it was extremely rare that a loss of control event was caused by unknown factors. The risks were generally well known within the organisation and their consequence was either ignored or normalised.

High performers had an embedded proactive and curious approach to risk where the assumption that tomorrow might well be a bad day was prominent whereas poor performing Companies had either a casual acceptance that bad things would inevitably happen from time to time, or an insistence that all bases were covered.

The Characteristics of the Three Culture Model

For each category I have listed a series of dominant characteristic behaviours with a focus on leading cultural indicators. I find the defining leading characteristics to be as follows.

DENIAL/RECKLESSNESS	ADMINISTRATIVE/NEGLIGENT	HIGH PERFORMANCE
Risks are obvious to a reasonable person	Risks are obvious to a skilled person	Risks are not obvious
A clear breach of duty	Failure to recognise a risk that should have been recognised	Almost unforeseeable
No meaningful investigations	Only seek primary cause	Investigations are deep
New ideas are actively discouraged	New ideas are seen as presenting problems	New ideas are welcomed
Managers do not want to know about problems	Reluctance to raise emerging risks	A belief that bad things are likely to happen
Managers have given up	Casual acceptance/Learned Helplessness	Strong proactive approach to risk identification and mitigation
Bad things frequently happen	Bad things that happen are due to known areas of risk	Bad things are very rare
Not Willing or Able	**Willing but not able**	**Willing and able**

What also emerged was evidence of a correlation between poor performing O&M organisations with the denial profile and high performing organisations with high performance characteristics. In studying the evidence of 12 Rail O&M Organisations in different countries and jurisdictions over a fifteen-year period I became convinced that there exists a clear cause and effect between the three Cultural Categories and performance outcomes.

If I was starting again, I would adopt this approach.

I would explain the features of each of the three-culture model to O&M Managers and invite them to evaluate themselves against each of the characteristics. A key feature of the model is the bottom one relating to the willingness and ability of managers with ability being directly related to the level of training that has been provided.

The quality of investigations, the degree of openness to new ideas and the extent to which management teams believe that things are going well have shown themselves to be very good leading indicators of the Organisation's culture. Look out for them.

CHAPTER NINETEEN

Denial or Professional Recklessness

Career Observations

This category is defined as being where a risk which would have been obvious to an interested person, not a skillful or trained one; where there was disregard of the need to take action, even when the risk and/or opportunity presented itself.

Victoria Station, London 1985/86

As a duty manager at London's Victoria Station, I put into action a core belief of mine, that managers should face the music and not leave it to the junior uniformed staff to receive the abuse and violence from passengers when services are disrupted. The various experiences would make a book on their own.

My practice was to go and stand near the most affected part of the ticket barrier line (Victoria had 18 platforms at that time) just before the announcement was made about late running or cancellations. What transpired was that I found myself standing at the same platform barriers almost every evening. There were deeply entrenched patterns of train running in the evening peak.

As I got to encounter more and more passengers, I became intrigued about their morning experiences which led to another key step. I got about

20 passengers collecting data for me about their morning trains which they claimed, 'were always late'.

What transpired was that there were entrenched patterns of late running in the morning peak too which, as a duty manager at Victoria, we were largely oblivious to because our focus in the morning peak was to get the arrived trains out to make space for more arrival trains. The late passengers were in a hurry and did not often stop to complain.

The data got me into charting the patterns of the rogue services. I persuaded my boss to allow me to do some field work at outstations to try to identify the source of the 'common cause' delays, the 'noise' which could not be attributed to a specific fault such as points or door failure.

The senior managers in Operations on the Southern Region were focused on the overall network number of 90% of trains running within 5 minutes of time which was achieved on most days when there was not a 'Special Cause' failure to blame and, as Jim Collins found, 'Good was the Enemy of the Great'. Nobody was interested in the missing 10%.

When I presented my analysis and findings at a Regional Operations Management forum I was shouted down. "How dare you have come to my area to look", was the Area Manager where there were repeated late starts on the same trains almost every day. "There is nothing wrong with any train running in my area" said another where one train had not started less than 6 minutes late on any day in over two months, despite the clarity of the findings. This personified entrenched denial combined with a low appetite.

Melbourne in the 2000s

The suburban system in Melbourne faced some major challenges in the 2000s although it started well with 3 years of record reliability after the completion of the Jolimont Rationalisation Project which gave Melbourne a large park between the city and the MCG on the banks of the Yarra river, coinciding with the early years of Franchising.

The franchises had been awarded with promises of extraordinary revenue growth which resulted in a commercial crisis in 2004 with one of the Operators walking away. At that point the Victorian Government decided to merge the two Operations back to one even though in the previous four years the train fleets had become incompatible with each other and the Operator who walked away had allowed their train driver numbers to fall well below the required number. As a consequence, even in good times the newly combined Network was under great pressure.

In 2004 an unprecedented increase in ridership began which lasted six years. Ridership almost doubled resulting in severe overcrowding in peak periods. The Government and the Operator failed to react until late 2007 by which time poor reliability had become a major media issue.

Why then is this period characterised as denial?

It seems to have been a failure of both the Operator and the Government to recognise that a new plan was required to free up more capacity and to procure more trains with the Operator being primarily responsible.

A Government Plan which they took to the 2007 State Government election called Meeting our Transport Challenges, which would have been better called Missing Our Transport Challenges, with funding for two major suburban rail projects that would not have provided a single additional train path. Neither progressed. There was also a significant expansion of the tram fleet promised but with no funding for a stabling or maintenance facility. Government 'own goals'.

In June 2008 the Operator and the State Agency developed a new Strategic Operating Plan to enable the network to be operated in a new five-Group rather than a traditional four-Group operation. By April 2010 the Operator, who had only recently been replaced, had done no work to prepare the detailed plans which would have enabled a new five-Group operation to be implemented. The first stage of the 2008 plan was subsequently implemented in May 2011 with other stages being implemented in 2012, two years later than was possible with significant reliability and customer satisfaction benefits to come.

A new Siemens train had been procured in the early 2000s but the drivers frequently experienced braking problems and lost confidence in the train. Within 12 months of the new Operator – MTM - being appointed, modifications to the braking system were made and driver confidence restored.

The Operator, during the period between 2005 and 2009 applied significant resources to attempting to get dispensation for events that were being deemed to be outside their control in an attempt to mask the underperformance. I am told that this emphasis is another practice from the UK franchising arrangements. It would have been better, in Melbourne's case, if they had done the analysis and developed a new plan but instead, they gave up and accepted the 'it's not our fault' position. Who did they think was going to fix it?

A Major Suburban Operator 2019

An in-depth review of a major suburban rail Operator revealed a culture of reliance on entrenched bias where not only was analysis not conducted but the refusal to acknowledge the findings once conducted and presented.

It was a culture as entrenched as in the UK's Southern Region in the mid-1980s where the Chief of Operations and also the head of Safety stated that the biggest obstacle to improving overall performance lay with public suicide prevention even though the analysis showed this was of only a minor importance.

Operation Near Miss: A new metro line opened in 2019

This Case Study highlights the risk of being committed to a date rather than being ready. It also reveals a series of catastrophic errors by many people and decisions who knew that things were badly wrong and were on the wrong path at least a year out from opening. Fortunately, there were no disastrous events, but this case combines the blindness of Thameslink 2018, the silo thinking of Kings Cross, the known non-compliance with requirements of Clapham and a casual reliance on hope, that they would get away with it, as the managers in BP Texas, and the RAF re Nimrod had.

Confidentiality Agreements prevents me from revealing the Line concerned but the conditions under which the new Line opened were quite extraordinary.

Firstly, not all of the safety critical systems had been commissioned including the emergency passenger communications systems between the

Control Centre and the trains. This was well known but the opening went ahead anyway. Where was the Regulator and the professional standards of both the Authority and the Operator, including their Board? They all continue to say that safety is their first priority! This problem had been one of the issues that held up the opening of the North East Line in Singapore in 2002. Neither the Authority (LTA) or the Operator, SBS Transit Rail, would allow it.

Secondly, the Rules and Operating Procedures were incomplete and known to be so. Consequently, the staff had not completed their training.

Thirdly, the staffing at stations was in line with the tender commitment but was known to be less than that required to fully implement the stations emergency management plans.

Fourthly, the period allocated for Trial Running was inadequate. In Singapore four GoA4 Lines which had been opened 9 stages experience had shown that a period of 12 weeks was required for Trial Running to enable the O&M staff to become both confident and competent in their handling of the new railway without passengers while also conducting many exercises for handling degraded and emergency operations. In this case less than 3 weeks was allowed even though none of the staff had any prior experience with a GoA4 system.

Fifthly, after operating for 6 months the CEO's stated priority was to reduce the resource levels to comply with the bid requirements, rather than overcoming many critical weaknesses. Eighteen months later, a new CEO reported that none of the major issues highlighted in an independent review conducted after 6-months of opening had been dealt with. Where was the Board? Where was the Regulator?

Were these risks well known? Yes, to all non-public stakeholders but the show had to, apparently, go on? Why? There wasn't even an election due within the next three years in that jurisdiction.

They are still getting away with it. When will the Swiss Cheese holes line up? Never hopefully but we want to call ourselves professionals.

On reflection, the lack of concern for the known risks was on a par with the 1980s practice of Cross-Channel Ferries entering the North Sea with their bow doors open to save time, despite the risk of flooding and capsizing as happened at Zeebrugge in March 1987 with 193 deaths.

I came to understand that, as a consequence

I came to believe that the Southern Region, Melbourne in the 2000s and the Major Operator's problem was one of denial, characterised by a refusal to look. Again, Deming sheds light on this in his fourth element, Knowledge of Psychology particularly the danger of reliance on entrenched bias and the openness, or not, to learning and improving.

Similarly, the long-term performance of Bukit Panjang LRT in Singapore, until a new Leader was appointed in 2017, had all the characteristics of 'a Denial culture'. That was a choice, as the subsequent improvement has shown when a determination to implement many of the high-performance characteristics was on display.

What I concluded from these cases that there was a conscious disregard of a substantial and unjustifiable risk to the customer, a lack of regard for the consequences of one's actions, or non-actions in these cases, where the senior management teams, allowed by their Regulators, deliberately and unjustifiably pursued a course of non-action and refusal to look.

I later read this which reinforced my thinking and practice

Track Worker Fatalities: Pasir Ris, Singapore

On 22nd of March 2016 two SMRT trainee track workers were on the main line tracks near Pasir Ris station on SMRT's East-West line along with 15 other track staff when they were struck by a train. They both died at the scene.

The key findings of the inquiry were that the failures were systematic and had occurred on many levels, that not only were the laid down Operating Procedures not followed but a completely different and clearly unsafe set of practices had also been adopted for the longest period of time. The official safety protocols were either unknown or completely disregarded.

The parties did not comply with the operating procedure. In fact, the procedure had not been complied with for many years. – Turner's incubation period.

This is another tragic case of the two-railway syndrome. The Rules requirements had been institutionally ignored and replaced by an unsafe, informal, unauthorised system of work. The non-compliance was widespread, with the

Safety Management System (Same as Nimrod), with the Rules and Procedure review (same as BP Texas), with monitoring etc.

How did the senior management not know? None were held accountable for the culture and malpractice. A senior manager was reported to say in a meeting in 2017 'that nobody follows any of the maintenance work instructions anyway' reflecting an established culture.

It would seem unlikely that it is a coincidence that reliability on several parts of that Rail Business had been poor for some years.

Thameslink, UK 2018

Back to the UK's old Southern Region. The introduction of the new service was a disaster. Extracts for reports in The Times highlight the main elements of what unfolded. The 1980s culture of Denial or professional recklessness and almost no accountability was on display.

Thameslink modernisation involved the expansion of the capacity of the Line through the middle of London to enable more and longer trains to operate on the corridor between Brighton on the South Coast and Bedford, north of London with new signalling technology in the core of the corridor.

According to report from The Times the Thameslink 2018 Industry Readiness Board had noted that of the 51 issues relating to the smooth running, 49 were considered to have been dealt with one month before opening. Industry leaders, backed by the Department for Transport believed that the changes were on course for a smooth launch on 21st May.

The Dept for Transport 'was advised by the industry in early May that they were ready for the new timetable'. 'Rail bosses congratulated themselves on a job well done' weeks before 20 May.

The Chair of the Office of the Rail Regulator, Prof Stephen Glaister concluded that there had been 'a failure to plan properly, that nobody took charge'. He concluded that the Dept for Transport, Network Rail, Train Operators had 'all made mistakes which contributed to the collapse of services' adding that 'risks were often underestimated or not understood at all because there were interdependencies and systemic in nature'.

'Nobody took charge'. Really? This 'we are all to blame' is a convenient way of treating accountability. The risks, as with Operation Near Miss with the new metro line in 2019 and in Queensland in 2016, were well known but the industry leaders ploughed on regardless. As we will see with NASA's fatal accidents in 1986 and 2003, and the

In respect to Rail reliability, it is not unusual to find similar belligerence. This part of the UK Rail Network includes the 1986 Southern Regional services where the senior management of the day were irritated when the repeating patterns of service failure were revealed. It is difficult to change entrenched cultures.

Nimrod Explosion 2006

A Nimrod XV230 exploded while on a reconnaissance flight in Afghanistan during refueling in 2006 resulting in 14 deaths. Charles Haddon-Cave QC led the Inquiry.

It revealed that the evidence was 'staring them in the face', but the RAF Managers chose not to see instead being determined to adopt a predetermined position that the fleet was safe. A bit like Operation Near Miss with the new metro Line in 2019.

The Nimrod fighter planes had been flying since 1969.Between 2001 and 2005 a Safety Review was conducted on the Nimrod where the focus was to demonstrate that the Nimrod was safe rather than to assess the risks and the relative control measures in place. The findings of that safety review was called a 'lamentable job'.

It led to the term the 'Fallacy of Safety' entering the vocabulary where organisations use documents to demonstrate that their safety arrangements were robust and effective rather than focusing on identifying the risks and ensuring that effective mitigation measures are in place.

The frequency of fuel leaks was over 40 times what was assumed in the Safety Case. The frequency of leaking fuel tanks in the Safety Case required a frequency of leaks to be improbable, 1 or 2 leaks during the operational life of the fleet yet between 2000 and 2005 there had been 40 fuel leaks per year. This data was available but had not been analysed. The worsening data trends had not been analysed over a six-year period! As with other cases, the data highlighting the risk was available and known but not acted upon.

Reflections

In each of the cases that I observed, and in the cases that I read about the characteristics of the Denial/Recklessness model were on display for interested eyes of the various Boards, senior managers, Regulators and Owners/Authorities. The characteristics of the Denial or Recklessness are often most openly displayed by the quality of investigations and the extent to which managers believe that the loss of control events are not their fault.

In each case it is difficult to conclude that the duty of care responsibility had not been discharged.

If I was starting again, I would adopt this approach.

As an O&M Manager once you are aware of a risk, taking no action is reckless. It is the same as Du Pont's well known saying in respect to safety that if you walk past an unsafe act or condition, you are endorsing it. The staff are always watching to gauge what the real standard is.

I would be alert to recklessness and denial once a proper analysis is conducted of performance at sub system level which provides opportunities for interested people to act.

CHAPTER TWENTY

Administrative or Professional Negligence

Career Observation

A sense that 'we're not too bad, certainly not the best, but generally acceptable' prevailed.

The key difference between this Administrative/Negligent culture and the Denial/Reckless culture is the extent to which the non-action was obvious to an interested person rather than a skillful trained person. What we see here are the problems associated with a casual laziness to not see and not act, often with tragic circumstances.

This casual laziness includes not acting or being seen to act on issues that come from within the organisation. This can include acting, or not on concerns or issues that emerge from field visits or from local investigations whose findings get passed up to senior managers. This is a significant tone setter. Are the senior management really listening and open to feedback or have they already decided on what action is to be taken? Administrative management prefers to push on with the normal rather than challenge it. Never mind the alternative, often inconvenient facts.

The Process Administrative manager often refers to the benefit of hindsight test. They knew but failed to act. This general slackness is the Normalisation of Deviance, the 'it will be alright on the night approach. These managers and their teams are not searching for areas of vulnerability and risk, they accept that things go wrong, that it is inevitable and by doing so refuse to recognise that loss of control events are a reflection on them, that they have failed.

The lack of a strong Business Rhythm, governance framework, is also important since it provides an opportunity to systematically check the health of things. In my experience when the reports always report very high compliance from Line Mangers the alarm bells ring.

It usually reflects a lack of attention to detail while monitoring or a deliberate failure to report risks and/or non-compliances upwards. That's why senior management need to conduct regular field visits to gest a sense of what is really happening but with a skeptical mindset.

As with Denial the quality of the investigations provides a key insight into the categorisation of the organisation. The level of ambition and the ease with which loss of control events are seen as being inevitable also provide a useful insight.

British Rail 1987

Low appetite, low resources and a general acceptance that poor performance was acceptable. The situation was grim. The irony is that the people who built and created the culture and exceptional performance in Hong Kong came from British Rail and London Underground. Quite interesting what a change in appetite and resources brings.

ScotRail Reliability 1991 to 1994

In ScotRail in 1991 I found that the local Operations Managers had no real understanding of how well the trains ran in their areas. Furthermore, what they 'knew to be true' before collecting data proved to be wrong. The old guard had incredible 'technical knowledge' regarding how the railway worked but little understanding. Something I have found everywhere else since, except perhaps in Sydney Trains.

The difference between the ScotRail team and the Southern Region management was that they had a hungry appetite, seemed motivated and took great pride in their work and its role in serving the public. They were willing and very able and a great deal was achieved.

The ScotRail managers knew their railway but did not understand it, how, why and where it did not work well. No analysis of patterns or trends that would provide what Demming called a key pillar of profound knowledge.

As we worked through a series of Line by Line analysis and our collective understanding improved, the self motivated, experienced managers resolved the multiple local problems that they had identified.

An article in the UK national paper, The Guardian wrote about the success that the ScotRail management team had. My contribution to the story was a quote that 'people get used to the trains being late and we have to do something about that'. The people I was referring to were the Operations managers.

ScotRail Investigations 1991 to 1994

We stopped ignoring and/or overruling findings from middle and junior managers.

Melbourne 1994

On arriving in Melbourne in 1994 I was told very assertively by the Operations Team that there was nothing wrong with the timetable design but that all the problems were caused by the unreliable trains. The Trains Team told me they needed to replace the whole traction system since that was the major reliability problem and if not, there was nothing much that could be done.

The peak reliability for about a decade had been about 86% within 5 minutes. There was a sense of helplessness rather than denial. As with the ScotRail team the appetite was high.

What soon transpired was that a high-level analysis showed that the timetable was unworkable in one of the four sectors of the network. Three sectors performed at a ten-year average close to 89% while one sector operated at approximately 78%.

With the Trains we found that a myriad of low-cost improvements on doors, air conditioning etc and some work place changes on how train faults were treated significantly improved train reliability.

After the timetable change in 1996 these changes led to a peak hour reliability of 93% in 1996/97 and a promise of a sustainable peak reliability over 95% after Jolimont Rationalisation. This was duly achieved after 2001 for a few years until external events introduced a period of instability and some loss of control.

The key difference between this case, ScotRail and BR Southern was the determination and desire to do much better and the openness to learning, a key behavioral trait of the characteristics of the prevailing culture there.

MTM 2012 to 2016 and SBS Transit Rail in 2015

Had a pathway to get peak reliability back to over 95% in peak periods but gave up the challenge after 2012, enough progress had been made. Good was the enemy of the Great.

In SBST in 2015 there was a sense that everything was fine, quite acceptable, that their performance far exceeded SMRT but thought that being as good as MTR in Hong Kong was out of the question.

I came to understand that, as a consequence

These cases highlight the problem arising when the view of the management is a sense that 'we're not too bad, certainly not the best, but generally acceptable' prevailed. There was an embedded failure to take proper care and a failure to exercise appropriate and/or ethical ruled care expected to be exercised amongst specified circumstances.

I later read this which reinforced my thinking and practice

The Piper Alpha Inquiry revealed that senior management were 'easily satisfied' that things were as they should be reflecting a lazy coziness that is also found in many Rail O&M companies regarding the systematic, proactive identification and management of risk.

The Kings Cross Fire Inquiry and Diane Vaughan's book about NASA's Challenger and Columbus accidents revealed the practice of senior managers ignoring recommendations and advice from middle and managers. Turner refers to this as the Normalisation Effect.

In NASA's case with the 1986 Challenger disaster the problems and the risks associated with the O rings was both well known and longstanding, but the risk of an explosion had become normalised. What Diane Vaughan wrote in her book was that NASA had not learned from this an predicted a repeat accident from similar underlying causes. She was proven to be correct when the Columbus Shuttle disintegrated on re-entering the atmosphere in 2003, caused by the damage to heat shields on the outside of the vehicle. Like the O ring this was a well known and longstanding problem

UK Health

The UK Health Inquiries particularly the Mid Staffordshire Inquiry in 2013 where Health Service Managers used the term 'with the benefit of hindsight' 501 times. The evidence was there for all curious eyes to see. He found that the main issues were cultural and included a lack of openness to criticism, an acceptance of poor standards, a failure to put patients first. The problems were found to be cultural, not medical.

In another Health Service case Ian Kennedy QC conducted a Public Inquiry in 1988 as to why so many babies under one were dying after cardiac surgery in Bristol Royal Infirmary where between 1986 and 1995 170 babies died who it was concluded, would have lived in another hospital.

He found that there was an old boys culture amongst the doctors, a lax approach to safety, secrecy about each Doctor's performance and lack of monitoring by Hospital managers. Sounds familiar.

Ladbroke Grove, UK 1999

The Ladbroke Grove inquiry in 1999 when a Reading bound train passed a signal at red, SN109 and crashed head on into a London bound train. 31 people died. The signal had a history of drivers passing it at red with 8 occurrences over the previous six years. The general picture, according to Cullen, was of 'a slack and complacent regime.'

While this is a safety incident the underlying problems with many rail and O&M managers that I have seen in respect to reliability are on display here. How many times did that signal need to be passed at red before management would have acted? Same question regarding the possible treatment of many known areas of reliability risk before and since.

The findings are very similar to those looking at poor rail reliability in Rail O&M organisations. The problems were cultural, not technical, including the 'old boys' culture as in Southern Region BR in 1986 and the UK Hospital Inquiries.

BP Texas: March 2005: 15 died

Warning signs of a possible disaster were present for several years but company officials did not intervene effectively to prevent it – US Chemical Safety and Hazard Investigation Board Report 2007. Following a shutdown for maintenance an explosion took place during the restart process. Fifteen people died.

The US Chemical Safety and Hazard Investigation Board Report 2007 conducted the Inquiry. They found that the 'warning signs of a possible disaster were present for several years, but company officials did not intervene effectively to prevent it'. They identified three key problems.

Firstly, that 'Employees frequently failed to comply strictly with procedures'.

Secondly, a problem with false certification. 'Procedures were certified annually as updated and complete by managers but without any attempt to verify with operational staff that procedures were adequate.

Thirdly, the combination of the two factors. The normalisation of the non-compliance with Procedures had combined with the slack approach to the review of Procedures. The absence of sufficient situational awareness, in this case not even following the Procedures and Rules when restarting the plant after maintenance, a well-known high-risk process.

As with other incidents the warning signs had been present for several years, for curious eyes. As in Piper Alpha the senior management must have been 'easily satisfied' that things were as they should be. This emphasises the importance of senior management setting the tone and culture.

Good to Great by Jim Collins

In his book Chapter One is titled that Good is the enemy of Great, that most organisations lose the hunger and drive to improve once their performance has reached a level where the stakeholders are satisfied. These include senior managers, Boards, Owners, the public, local media and Regulators.

In Australia the stakeholders in Sydney and Perth have a much higher expectation of performance than in Melbourne. I suggest that this is borne out Sydney and Perth delivering very high levels of sustained performance for many years. Similarly in the UK, the long term reliability enjoyed by Mersey Rail and City to Sea are seen as outliers where their circumstances are seen as making the task easy.

In 2015 in Singapore, the Rail Operators had the same opinion regarding MTR's performance in Hong Kong, but not anymore.

If I was starting again, I would adopt this approach.

The motivation to create a desire to deliver excellence can be found by looking to create career highlights for many of the people including senior managers and their teams. In 2015 in SBS Transit Rail only one of the senior management team of six had enjoyed a career highlight in the previous decade. How sad. The improvement in reliability since 2016 has certainly filled that gap, not only for them but for hundreds of people in their teams.

Get your team to come to terms with what the legal requirement of 'taking all reasonable steps' actually means, particularly the question of the acceptability of known causes of predictable loss of control events.

While this raises the issue of appetite it also includes the question of discipline and the extent to which teams are always in a state of having to react compared to being proactive and in control.

CHAPTER TWENTY ONE

High Performance Cultures

Career Observations

Melbourne 1997

By December 1997 the Met Trains organisation was open to all sorts of possibilities. A pathway to get to peak hour reliability of 95% was being delivered.

MTR Hong Kong

MTR has been well served by a series of great forward-looking leaders; Roger Kyneston, Phil Gaffney and Andrew McCusker. A culture for looking further that the rest had been established and improved upon over 20 years.

The reliance on analysis, risk identification, mitigation plans were deeply embedded in safety, asset condition, competence, emergency readiness. There were no short cuts.

By 2010, the systematic analysis of asset reliability and condition at asset level, sub system level, and key component level went far beyond what was being done in Singapore and the reliability, asset performance and reputation for excellence created credentials which have been industry leading.

In 2003 SMRT and Hong Kong MTR were very comparable. By 2010 SMRT had a declining MKBF of about 100k, and an asset base which had been badly run down leading to the asset emergency which became apparent in 2011 and took eight years to rectify, while MTR's MKBF was close to 800k.

An irony: The question mark about MTR must be the performance of their Operations in Australia which do not reflect the level of excellence that is found in Hong Kong.

Singapore 2014 to 2021

SBS Transit Rail's MKBF 2014-2020 improved from 199k in 2014 to 2.1m in 2021, having exceeded 1 million for 4 years. The six foundations of excellence were there. The changes in 2015 and 2016 were brought about through a changed appetite, governance and improved analysis. The rest was easy.

SMRT Rail's MKBF had risen from 100k in 2014 to 1.4m in 2021 while their Bukit Panjang LRT had undergone an even more remarkable transformation. This improvement was characterised by having a very high understanding of performance and risks and had plans, where investigations became deep and multi-level ownership emerged.

As with Melbourne in 1994 there were significant underlying system design problems, but it did not stop the new BPLRT management team from improving discipline, analysis, investigations and picking the abundant low hanging fruit that was available. That is the job. The BPLRT MKBF improved from 25k in 2014 to a 12-month moving average of 250k in 2021

I came to understand that, as a consequence

In the above cases the characteristics of High Performance were evident based on ambition, discipline, skill, careful attention to warning signs and a multi layered team-based commitment where all the insights and experience were respected and welcomed. The brains were turned on.

The significant benefit from basic applied statistical analysis, not only as a basis of much improved performance but also of improved capability, pride and ambition were also evident. The power of properly conducted analysis to release the latent capabilities of the various teams and leaders at multiple levels of the organisation revealed itself.

The opportunity to learn from investigations and audit took me a long time to grasp. Their insights often highlight inconvenient truths. In time I also came to appreciate the importance of contemporary thinking. For me James Reason has ben a source of wisdom and reflection as has the concept of loss control.

Beyond this the studying of many Independent Inquiries provide a valuable source of 'there but for the grace of God go I' moments. I remember hearing how the Signalling Engineers had failed after the Clapham Junction Inquiry report was published in 1989 while thinking that an in-depth review of my stewardship of my own responsibilities would show similar, if not worse failings.

Elsewhere in the book I have described how we approached the various obligations and challenges in SBS Transit Rail between 2015 and 2017. It was later as I refined the characteristic of the three-culture model that I came to see that we had been moving to a new normal where the characteristics of the High Performing Company became entrenched. I am very proud of having helped to shape their journey but more so of its sustained excellence under Leong Yim Sing, who was the first to say I should write this book, and Jeffrey Sim who was a key player in getting the ball rolling.

Reflections on Cultural Categories

The opportunity to encourage curiosity and ownership always presents itself, to emulate Sir Isaac Newton's saying, that 'if I have seen further than the rest it is because I have been standing on the shoulders of giants'.

In a sense the SBS Transit Rail journey was a culmination of everything that I had learned since 1982 particularly from Melbourne in the 1990s, the Olympic Rail Task 1997 to 2000 and various short term interim management and Advisory roles between 2007 and 2014 and after 2017.

It is quite understandable that readers may be shocked by the Recklessness and Negligence terms, but I challenge the reader to consider how else they should be treated.

As an industry we allow the characteristics of Denial to be quite common. When this is allowed by CEO's Boards, Regulators, State Authorities and/or Owners I believe that they do the industry a great disservice.

I suggest that high performance is not easy, but many parts of companies achieve it. Unfortunately, however within Rail we seem to celebrate 'giving it our best shot' as a substitute for effective management of risk.

If I was starting again, I would adopt this approach.

Teams need a mission, and it needs to be about exceeding all reasonable expectations. Ipswich electrification, Melbourne reliability in the 1990s, the Sydney Olympic Rail Task in 2000, the start up of the North East Line and the SBS Transit Rail reliability journey after 2015 are all great examples of it.

Nealy everybody wants to be part of a great mission particularly to be involved in its development and delivery. Almost everybody has valuable insights and experience. Ignore them at your peril.

The must be a determination to be proactive and to take all reasonable steps and not to accept that 'bad things' are ever inevitable.

Teams are generally knowledgeable but also need to be skillful. There is a need for disciplined internal processes of review based on valid techniques whether applied to analysis, investigation.

PART FOUR: Technical Excellence: The Operator's Challenge

This section looks at the criticality of maintaining the interfaces within and between the three sectors of the Operator's Challenge and the required scope and discipline about how to use the Modification Control Process to aid the O&M Manager in this challenge.

As with applied statistical analysis, Investigations, and an understanding of loss control theory it was through experience that I became introduced to Modification Control despite its importance. O&M Managers not being trained illustrates the lack of either understanding or implication of Reason's Swiss Cheese model.

This section looks at the normal range of typical risks that are to be found within each of the three Sectors in every rail system: assets and systems, rules, operating procedures and work instructions and competence and confidence of people. For each risk control measures which have been shown to be effective are provided for reference.

CHAPTER TWENTY TWO

How "Railways die at their interfaces"

The problematic delivery of major projects in the UK for both Thameslink in 2017 and Crossrail 2018 and the relatively problem free startup of new lines in Singapore in 2003 and 2015/17 highlight the critical importance of system thinking. Similarly, the successful transformation of rail reliability in Singapore since 2015 reflects a stronger emphasis on system thinking and analysis.

Career observations

Timetable Design

Railways work well when all the parts are in sync with each other, and that the train movement is able to flow without what I came to regard as turbulence. At Ipswich I realised that our obligation was to ensure our trains got to Colchester in their slot so that additional trains from Clacton, Colchester, Southend Victoria etc could enjoy their slots

In many Networks I have found that that the timetable design often meets some predetermined rules that don't represent a working reality. This was the case in the Southern Region in 1985 but I discovered that nobody was allowed to say that the plan was unworkable.

While timetable design is a very important factor precise execution of the plan is also fundamental requirement of both safe and high performance.

Metro Railways

The systems interface challenge is more complex than in suburban or InterCity railways because of their nature as integrated engineering systems but the basic requirements are the same.

The three segments

This section is mainly concerned with the foreseeable and common risks that are found within each segment and provides some examples on how they can be well mitigated.

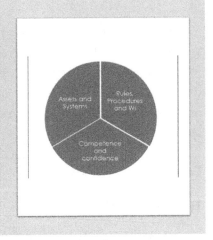

Maintaining Tight and Functional Interfaces

- Every Network has 34 Common Risks
- 7 in Assets and Systems
- 10 in Rules and Procedures
- 9 in Competence
- 6 in Modification Control of changes within and between any of the three sectors

As with other parts of this book, it highlights the need for a system to ensure that each risk area is assessed and that risk mitigation measures are adjusted accordingly.

The Modification Control Procedure and discipline are critical to ensure that as one risk control measure is adjusted the others with which it interfaces are adjusted too. High safety, asset performance and reliability rely on it to ensure that risk control barriers are kept in sync and healthy.

Without a management system and high discipline the health of the risk control measures deteriorate. The complacency risk coupled with the 'management can be easily satisfied that things are as they should be' malaise remain outside the specific risks within and between each sector.

The skeptical mindset and Business Rhythm are designed to assist the O&M Manager here.

Sir Peter Parker, British Rail Chairman 1976 to 1983, used to talk about railways failing at their interfaces. I came to understand that he was correct.

Mark Wild, CEO of Crossrail spoke of the lack of understanding of the system thinking in the design and procurement of Crossrail. The unnecessary complexity of the design and short-sighted procurement decisions left the integration challenge as an unseen risk. It led significantly to a three year delay and £4bn overrun.

I came to understand that, as a consequence

The Organisational Culture Reveals Itself

The listed risks within each segment are generally well known. If senior managers are 'easily satisfied' that the controls are satisfactory is that a reflection of an Administrative, negligent senior management? I think so.

If senior managers are aware that the asset condition is deteriorating fast, that 'my people do not follow or know' the Working Instructions, that there are no action plans to prevent recurrence of loss of control events is that a reflection of Denial or recklessness by senior management? I think so.

That change requires a certain mindset that accepts that 'holes' are lurking, that the designed control barriers are probably not as healthy as performance suggests, a permanent sense of unease.

The Business Processes and Systems were designed to enable a skeptical, risk searching, 'brains turned on' at multiple levels, culture to emerge, a High Performing culture. One where investigations were undertaken with follow up actions to ensure the likelihood of recurrence was SFAIRP. It recognises that ALARP may have not been good enough.

As I reflected on my experiences and reading followed by a series of seminars on O&M rail management my cultural categorisation became clearer. Whilst it was safety incidents that helped to shape my thinking what I discovered was that organisations where denial and administrative character-istics were found were also those that had the worst safety records.

Since 2009 I have had the opportunity to study in some detail the O&M of twelve different Rail O&M organisations, finding strong evidence of denial in six, administration in four and two of high performance. That their reliability and safety performance has reflected that categorisation is not surprising.

Within each segment I highlight common risks and challenges with main-taining 'healthy' barriers, 34 in total but exclude repeating references to what I have called the Universal Obligations of O&M management.

That system thinking is required but is not well understood or discussed.

When British Rail's Mechanical and Electrical Engineers became aware of the problems with trains sliding after the disc braked trains were introduced, they were allowed to transfer the responsibility for mitigating that risk to the train driver's managers and the tree and vegetation clearance gangs. Hardly effective system thinking or management.

By 2002 when I developed the three-segment model to explain the chal-lenge of ensuring the integrity of the multiple interfaces I had come to under-stand that it was not only the integrity of each part but of the system as a whole where the devils lurked.

The environment: The Local Political and Social Conditions

While the O&M challenges are the same in similar types of railways the local Legal, Social and Political conditions are not. Singapore's environment is not the same as an Australian, a British or a Middle Eastern one. The local socio/political culture sets the context in which the O&M Manager has to op-erate.

While in Australia the typical 'she'll be right mate' culture sets a certain expectation in Singapore this is not the case. That is not to say that Australia is always like that since without high levels of capability, skill and discipline the heavy freight railways in Western Australia would not be world leading as they are from an engineering and O&M perspective.

If I was starting again, I would adopt this approach.

As with other matters related to technical capability, this system thinking needs to be promoted and taught.

As we work through this section the normal risks within each segment are found to be many and complex, but the integration risk is even larger since a change in one sub-segment necessarily requires an assessment and an adjustment of the designed control measures in other sub segments and often the other segments too.

Who knew? A foreseeable risk? Yes, for interested, curious eyes.

CHAPTER TWENTY THREE

Asset Management: Seven Common Risks

*T*his section identifies seven recurring areas of risk in Asset Management, each requiring careful monitoring and control to prevent loss of control events. This section identifies these risks and shares a set of control measures which have been shown to prevent loss of control events, which have enabled Managers to become more confident about predicting future performance.

The seven common areas of risk in this segment emerge from the following:

- Firstly, assets and Systems do not fail as expected even on Day One, or, secondly after the Defect Liability Period (DLP) has expired through the long asset life.
- The OEM Major Periodic Maintenance plans are often conservative providing both risks and opportunities.
- The provision of inadequate Tools and Test Equipment
- People take short cuts and informal working methods emerge, the two-railway syndrome.
- Changes in Maintenance Plans need to be checked and promulgated properly.

- Senior, unqualified staff deciding what action should be taken in response to asset failures before any investigation has been undertaken.

One: The Assets and Systems do not behave and fail as expected, even on Day One after integrated commissioning.

The risk

Leaving aside acknowledged asset and system defects associated with new assets and systems, 'holes in the cheese' are found to be to be present from Day One. The failure patterns and the required mitigation plans are not in line with O&M manual specifications.

How to mitigate the risk

During DLP, asset and systems are likely to require tweaks to the commissioned systems to improve the design of the integrated engineering systems in light of experience.

Performance including wear and tear is also likely to require adjustments to the scope and frequency of Planned Maintenance (PM) schedules as risks and challenges emerge. This is normal. The OEM Supplier does not get everything right.

If those careful adjustments are not made, the 'holes' open up. The more that happens the more likely that 'loss of control' events will occur.

Under the section dealing with Modification Control the need to approve and promulgate these associated changes is dealt with.

Two: The Assets and Systems do not fail or behave as expected through their working lives.

The risk

During the working life assets and systems display wear and tear and patterns of failure that are different to those expected by the OEM Suppliers. This is not a phenomenon only in the DLP. This provides a more complex set of challenges since some components, sub-systems or whole systems wear both faster and slower than expected and also display patterns of failure than expected which can present challenges at the interfaces with other parts of a system.

Failing to adjust the scope and frequency of the PM programme in line with emerging analysis of failure patterns and condition reports is common and allows 'holes' to open up. The more that happens the more likely that 'loss of control' events will occur.

Changes need to be made to the PM scope or schedule to keep abreast of the emerging 'holes' in the cheese.

The early identification of these 'holes' and their subsequent control is a major challenge to the O&M Manager. The Manager needs to be alert to these challenges and act accordingly.

How to mitigate the risk

Without a timely adjustment of the PM scope and schedule 'holes' can emerge and grow.

Without a strong review and approval of change mechanism the actual PM scope and schedule can allow 'holes' to emerge and grow.

Without a well structured change promulgation regime the general knowledge and understanding of the staff can fall, allowing 'holes' to emerge and grow.

Three: OEM recommended Major Periodic Maintenance (MPM) requirements are known to often be conservative.

The risk and opportunity

This conservatism is well known and contributes to complacency regarding strict compliance. The business and asset management opportunity is to push the timing and scope of PM schedules out, including overhauls, to save money.

The risk is that insufficient care is taken to ensure that asset condition and performance risks are carefully identified and monitored through this process.

The pushing out of MPM schedules generally has no short term consequence because of the relatively long life cycle of the components and systems. Unless carefully managed it can easily result in fund-deprived Asset

Managers overseeing a deteriorating asset condition. The consequences may remain, the latent conditions, for several years.

How to mitigate the risk

There are proven methods for pushing out MPM scope and schedules using samples of the asset class to ensure that condition and performance risks are under control and properly understood.

Four: Inadequate Tools and Test Equipment

The risk

That maintenance staff are not provided with adequate tools to do their job properly and/or that such equipment is not well maintained or calibrated properly.

How to mitigate the risk

Bad workmen blame their tools, but the opposite is also true. If staff are not well equipped, it is difficult for them to do an outstanding job.

Proper registers regarding tool calibration should be available for tools such as torque wrenches and for maintenance of other precision tools and test equipment. They should be checked by senior management regularly. The staff notice.

In SBS Transit, the provision of high-quality diagnostic equipment in respect of the Overhead Line and P'Way, the linear assets, enabled a transformation in understanding and intervention. In both cases, the ambition and sense of pride of the affected maintenance groups was noticeably enhanced.

The provision and maintenance of proven but leading-edge technology by the management sends a clear message regarding appetite and seriousness about quality standards and risk identification and control. As with keeping the tools correctly calibrated and in good condition the staff notice, it affects their level of engagement.

Five: Maintainers take short cuts and informal, unknown methods of work become established.

The risk

The taking and widespread adoption of short cuts creates the two-railway syndrome which can result in documented Procedures and Work Instructions becoming obsolete. The Track Fatalities, BP Texas and Piper Alpha provide examples of Informal methods of work resulting in tragic accidents.

However, non-compliance with recommended PM schedules or with changed but authorised PM schedules are also a common risk.

This can often be caused by lack of funding, time, spares and tools, or poor training, supervision and monitoring. Either way, it is management's responsibility to ensure these things do not happen.

How to mitigate the risk

This is covered in detail under the sections on Rules, Procedures and Work Instructions and also under Competent, Confident People.

Case Studies: Singapore – SMRT and SBS Transit Rail

In 2017, a senior SMRT Maintenance Director stated that 'nobody follows the Work Instructions'. Falsification of maintenance records was also discovered to be a problem. No systematic formal review and authorisation of changes in PM scope and schedule was in place.

Leaving aside SMRT's experience there was also evidence of this latent condition in SBST in 2015 where a major requirement of the LRT recommended PM cycle had been ignored due to a lack of review of the plan against the OEM's recommendation, perhaps enabled by a determination not to increase resources on the basis that 'things are not too bad'.

In SBS Transit Rail's case, as a direct consequence of this omission, there were some bad failures in 2015 whose consequences could have been much worse. Precursor events of bad times ahead unless a much more informed, thorough and proactive approach was adopted.

With much improved approach in both organisations, not only has asset condition and reliability been transformed but so has safety.

Six: Changes in Maintenance Plans and Practices are not properly checked or promulgated, communicated to the staff who need to know and apply the changed practice.

<u>The risk</u>

That changes to the PM scope and/or schedule are not understood or complied with.

<u>How to mitigate the risk</u>

See good practice Case Study below.

Changes in Maintenance Plans need to be checked and promulgated properly.

I will deal with the importance of Modification Control in chapter twenty five but when changing PM practices, the case study below provides a well developed framework.

Case Study: A Good Practice in Managing Changes in Maintenance Practices

The importance of Modification Control is dealt with a bit later but when changing PM practices, it has a rarely understood importance.

A change in the PM scope or frequency is a deliberate change to the designed risk control measures.

A good practice is to have a second person check to review the evidence and the basis for the change and that the likelihood that the change will be successful in its objectives.

The second person check ensures that the proposed change dos not introduce other 'holes' as the current risk mitigation measure is modified.

In a good practice framework the Departmental Head

- Had to recommend the change and get the Head of Engineering, who had specific responsibility for ensuring that the overall integration of the respective control measures was fit and complete, to approve it, or not.

- Had to ensure that the Maintenance Manuals and Work Instructions are updated to ensure their ongoing correctness. The Departmental Head's responsibility in SBS Transit Rail.

- Had to ensure that any training material is updated. The Departmental Head's responsibility where the Head of Department is responsible for determining competence standards and for final assessments.
- Had to ensure that the staff are made aware of the change.

Why were these the specific responsibility of the Department Head rather than a support Department?

- The Department Head, under the Law, is responsible for the System of Work, the Competence of the Staff, including Contractors, for monitoring compliance and taking corrective action when non-compliances are identified.
- Keep the accountabilities clear.

A good practice is to have three categories of change based on risk.

- Category A was minor, and changes could be shared at shift briefings.
- Category B change was significant and required formal briefing to all affected staff before the change was made and
- Category C change was major and required retraining before the change was made.

In each case, following the change there was a duty on supervisors to check compliance with the new requirement.

The Departmental Head's responsibility

- That a history of change file is updated, ensuring that successors can see and understand the history.
- This may seem onerous but without it the 'as-is' state can become quite different to the documented state and the two-railway syndrome quickly emerges.
- It is up to the skill of the Maintenance Mangers to ensure that these steps are both performed but are not overly bureaucratic which makes full compliance too arduous and less likely to be complied with.

Seven: Senior, unqualified staff deciding what action should be taken in response to asset failures before any investigation has been undertaken.

<u>The risk</u>

You don't think this happens? It happens a lot, truly. Even worse, the 'guilty' senior staff are almost always wrong. Its cultural consequence is to reduce the need for proper investigations, and it reduces the accountability on expert managers to create preventative action plans, leaving aside the absurdity of it.

It prevents proper learning and sets such a bad example.

<u>How to mitigate the risk</u>

The organisational Processes and Systems and Business Rhythm are designed to prevent this from occurring.

Having a commitment to properly investigate loss of control events, to identify the weaknesses in the Organisational barriers to ensure that action plans look to strengthen those barriers, or prevent recurrence, is paramount.

This requires a sound methodology, effective training in the methodology and a commitment from senior managers to commit resources to prevent recurrence. Not that common, unfortunately.

Achieving sustainable High Performance in Asset Management has challenging requirements

These include:

- A high-quality application of the requirements of the Universal Obligations of O&M management – to ensure that the 'right things are being done' rather than complying with laid down requirements, 'doing the right things'.
- Maintaining accurate Planned Maintenance documentation including formal review and authorisation of any changes.
- Maintaining accurate Procedures and Work Instructions as changes to the Planned Maintenance regime are made, including meaningful reviews and verification with users.

- Increased monitoring of staff after changes have been made to ensure that the new requirements are understood and are being effective in achieving their objective.
- Training and Assessment documentations being maintained in a healthy state as changes to the Planned Maintenance regime are made.
- Maintaining an accurate record, a Knowledge Journey document, so that successors can understand the basis of the decision making that led to the current Planned Maintenance Plan scope and schedule...........

What has this got to do with reliability?

Loss of control events are usually associated with discussions related to safety but failures in service delivery have the same sources, a failure to understand and manage the universal obligations of O&M management.

In the same way that major accident investigations reveal many cultural shortcomings, investigations into poor reliability are the same. The universal obligation remain; to understand the underlying performance and condition, particularly at sub system and key component level, the identification of risks and the introduction of risk mitigation measures.

In operations the design of the timetable, its operability on the fixed infrastructure and the precision of the execution of the plan are critical. With assets the underlying principles are the same; there is a need to understand performance in a granular sense, often at sub system or key component level and to proactively intervene to minimise the likelihood of loss of control events, failures that result in delays.

Good practice has identified three areas of intervention for asset managers and maintainers.

Reliability mitigation measures can be put into three categories:

One: Changing the scope and schedule of the Planned Maintenance regime.

In my experience the 'experts' within Asset Teams, including supervisors and more technically qualified engineers are best placed to collaborate to share insights to identify what changes can have greatest effect. This can have four significant impacts:

- A dramatic improvement in underlying performance with reduced failures.
- These improvements are often free.
- Embedding multi-layer Leadership where different experts can bring their brains and insights to the task. It builds individual and collective confidence and turns the brains on at the gate, rather than turning them off.

Two: Changing out components.

This can treat clearly defined problems, can be quite expensive but provide significant benefits.

A key question is how many times can a particular asset or component fail before a system wide changeout is made. In the reliability drive in SBS Transit Rail we encouraged Asset Managers to be less cautious about seeking funding to change out failing components. It helped to reset the tone, the expectation, the latent mindset about what senior management wanted.

Was it expensive? Sometimes. Worth it? Going from 21 delays per year over 5 minutes to only one or two has become normal. Who has to become used to, or not, trains running late? In ScotRail and Singapore I think it was the senior managers first. The community at large benefitted from it.

Three: Enhancing the design.

This can be very expensive and can take a long time but is sometimes necessary.

A Case Study: MTR, Hong Kong: The world's best O&M Manager?

Hong Kong's MTR were the first railway to achieve accreditation in Asset Management. Their objective was to better understand the performance and condition of their assets underpinning better reliability and more predictable asset management throughout the whole life cycle.

In 2008, under Andrew McCusker's leadership, as a result of their improved understanding of asset condition and performance at asset, sub system, key component levels they were able to assert that they would aim to extend the working life of all assets 50% beyond their design life without any reduction in reliability delivering significant reductions in life cycle costs.

The strength of their systems engineering approach across all their asset management risks areas, their depth in respect of the six universal obligations of O&M Management has enabled them to lead Rail O&M thinking for over 20 years.

MTR demonstrated a relentless search for improvement in everything they do, an example that SBS Transit Rail adopted after 2015.

Rules, Procedures and Work Instructions: Ten Common Risks

*R*ules, Procedures and Work Instructions are not supposed to be complex and mysterious, requiring semi legal discussions between interested parties regarding their nuances and understanding.

They are there to prescribe a safe, efficient, and effective method or working. That's all.

This section identifies ten recurring areas of risk in Asset Management, each requiring careful monitoring and control to prevent loss of control events. It identifies these risks and shares a set of control measures which have been shown to target loss of control events, which have enabled Managers to become more confident about predicting future performance.

Introduction

While an earlier section discusses the cultural norms and recognises the predominance of the Administrative culture where most people are going through the motions, sustainable high performance requires a well-structured, disciplined framework and timetable of activities, a management system including monitoring of compliance and follow up.

Without such a system, maintaining a sustainable high-performance culture is impossible.

Experience shows that there are some common sources of risk with the Operating Rules, Procedures and Work Instructions.

This section attempts to identify those risks and proposes mitigation measures.

The Ten Risks

We know that the following is almost certainly the case:

- Rules, Procedures and Work Instructions are:
  - Not readable,
  - Not easily understood.
  - Not properly reviewed despite the commitment in Safety Policies and Systems.
  - Not validated to ensure that they are safe, efficient and workable.
  - Not followed by the staff.
  - Not sufficiently complete with missing steps.
  - Not monitored.
  - Not practiced for degraded and emergency scenarios creating a false sense of 'readiness'.
- There at risk Procedures exist. Procedures that many of the staff do not know or understand properly.
- Changes to Rules, Procedures and Work Instructions (R&P&WI) need to be reviewed and approved carefully, and once approved promulgated properly in line with their risk category.

One: The R&P& WI: Not readable

The risk

I once received a revised R&P change to authorise which had been through the Modification Control Process. It was 26 pages long and, after three attempts - unreadable yet it was for front line staff to understand and follow.

How to mitigate the risk

The subsequent internal debate was fascinating. Many people had a stake including safety professionals and trainers. They wanted a to see all the hazard analysis and underlying information that auditors and trainers wanted to reference.

A new process was developed for refining all Procedures.

- Each Procedure was to have a reference file with all the background information that the Auditors and Trainers wanted to have as supporting material which was subject to a rigorous Modification Control Process, the same as the R&P&WI itself.

- Each Procedure was to have a checklist of tasks for the front line staff with dos and don'ts. These checklists were put through the User Verification Process as part of the Validation process.

The objectives were satisfied. A programme for all Procedures was drawn up for conversion. The other advantage of this approach was that the Supervisors and Managers had a much more explicit document to use for ongoing assessment and reinforcement of knowledge purposes.

On reflection, the previous approach of making available 26 or even 52 pages of background documents to them was bound to result in the two railway syndrome.

It showed how senior managers can 'dump' a huge problem of understanding and compliance on front line staff, hardly good for the one-team of multiple layers of ownership that high performance requires. It is similar to giving maintainers bad, uncalibrated, poorly maintained tools to do their job properly.

Two: R&P & WI: Not understood

The Risk

The written Rules and Procedures are supposed to prescribe a safe, efficient, effective method of work. They need to be accessible, readable and practical. In the UK in 1992 an Independent Study of British Rail's R&P identified two critical findings:

- That the average adult reading age was of a 9 year old.

- The required reading age for BR's R&P was a 22 year old.

On reflection, while this was shocking to learn it was not surprising when I reflected on the legal type discussions of the nuances of different R&P between interested managers.

The requirement of being readable and practical left me wondering. In Melbourne and Sydney between 1994 and 2000 the same legal type debates continued, the irony of the gap between the requirement to provide clear, practical R&P to the workforce being lost on the 'lawyers'.

How to Mitigate the Risk

New Procedures were developed in a much simpler format, as explained under the previous risk.

Each Procedure had a checklist of tasks for the front line staff with dos and do nots. These checklists were put through the User Verification Process (see risk five in this chapter) as part of the Validation process.

Three: The R&P&WI: Not reviewed

The Risk

Most railways have a two or three year review requirement.

Most Railways have over 300 Rules, Procedures and/or Work Instructions and a commitment in their Safety Management Systems to review them every two or three years.

I am always interested in the register of review. It is quite normal to find compliance of about 75% and to see dozens of review dates being the same – both warning signs that a desk based process is in play.

The investigation into the 2005 BP Texas explosion revealed that the approach to reviewing and re-certifying the specific R&P&WI was casual and did not involve any checks against the actual working methods or those that had to apply them.

How to mitigate the risk

In SBS Transit Rail there was a timetable each month for three years with Rules, Procedures and Work Instruction review dates. Typically, Department Heads had to handle approximately two items per week over a 36 month cycle.

Every second cycle a User Verification Check was required involving the users with a desk top and in-field review to avoid the situation where 'nobody follows the Work Instructions anyway'. It also helps the Departmental Head to have a high level of working knowledge through this mechanism. Two items per months lends itself to an ongoing process as part of the normal Business Rhythm.

Four: The R&P&WI: Not validated

<u>The Risk</u>

Rules, Procedures and Work Instructions are usually drafted from Design documentation or taken from OEM Supplier documents. Often, when tried in the field shortcomings - including lack of impracticality - emerge. If this is not dealt with at source, informal, unauthorised work practices evolve and quickly become normalised within the workplace.

The findings into the Pasir Ris and BP Texas accidents found that two common failings:

- That the R&P had not been followed for many years, and that the R&P were impractical and unworkable. Consequently, left to their own devices the staff had established their own informal methods of work.

So why is this process not common? It is expensive in its use of busy experts. It requires a rare appetite, discipline and commitment - a high performance culture.

<u>How to mitigate the risk</u>

In SBST in 2002 in light of the above risk a 'User Verification Process' was embarked upon. We took the complex, multi-user party R&P and adopted a process which included the following:

The Group included the writer of the specific R&P, the users (front line workers including OCC staff), the trainer to ensure that any changes would be able to be cascaded properly and a representative from Safety to ensure that the integrity of the Hazard Log was maintained with any changes. The team went through a two-step process involving a desk top study followed by an in-field application.

In every case the R&P was subject to significant change to ensure safety, practicality and efficiency. It typically meant the addition and removal of specified steps.

It was felt that by having R&P that met the requirements of being safe, efficient and practical it was likely that the staff would follow them (no unnecessary or impractical steps) and that the Departmental Manager would have a strong ownership of their content.

In 2016, after the fatal accident at Pasir Ris on SMRT's East-West Line several in-depth checks of compliance with the SBST R&P, both internally and externally, found compliance to be exceptionally high. The User Verification Process played a large role in this.

Except SBS Transit Rail, I am not aware of any other Operator who carries out user verification as a matter of course.

Five: R&P&WI not followed

The risk

That informal methods of work become normalised. The tendency to have two systems of work is common.

This first came to my notice after the Clapham Train Crash in London in 1988. The senior, mostly office bound managers thought that the written R&P were in place, but the outside staff and supervisors were doing something else.

The extent to which this is common is debatable but a review of bad events, and my observed experience suggests that it is common as highlighted in the following:

- 'Nobody follows any of the Maintenance Work Instructions — everybody knows that'. A senior Maintenance Manager in one railway in 2017.
- The informal methods of work in place at Texas BP.
- The incompleteness and casual non-compliance with the R&P at Piper Alpha.
- The deliberate ignoring of R&P at Zeebrugge

How to mitigate the risk

A good practice is where the Safety Policy specifies that the Heads of Departments were specifically responsible for a number of things including the following:

- There having to be a safe system of work.
- That their staff and contractors were properly trained and assessed.
- That they monitored compliance with the above requirements.
- That they recorded and took the necessary corrective action.

The whole philosophy is based on the dozen or so Departmental Heads having these specific responsibilities. The senior manager's roles are to ensure that the serious risk and consequences of the two-railway syndrome are well understood.

Observation in the field both formal and casual along with regular visits to worksites by Senior Managers provided the opportunity to highlight the risks and to set the expectations.

At staff inductions on their first day, when people are probably at their most alert, tell new staff two things:

- That people who take shortcuts with Procedures won't be allowed to stay employed because of the risk to themselves and their new colleagues.
- That if they are unsure about what to do, to ask. That we gave no prizes for guessing. That they should 'never assume, always ensure'.

These simple messages should be reinforced at staff briefings and during training.

Six: R&P&WI not tight enough

The risk

That the R&P&WI are incomplete leaving holes in the barrier they were intended to create.

The Glenbrook train crash in Sydney in December 1999 occurred when a train had been authorised to pass the previous signal at red and then crashed into a train in the section ahead which the train driver had not expected to be there, nor had the authorising signalman.

In the Inquiry much was made of the understanding of the respective regulation allowing trains to pass red signals and the maximum speed allowed by the Procedure. The discussion and the various pieces of evidence led to the conclusion that the relevant R&P was far from universally understood.

In the British Rail R&P from the 1970s the signalman had to use the words when giving permission for a driver to pass a red signal that 'you can pass that signal at red/danger but must obey all others'. In the Glenbrook case the driver had implicitly been led to believe that the section ahead was clear.

By contrast, the BR Rule for the train driver was 'to proceed with caution and be able to stop short of any obstruction' which set a viewing distance based allowable speed.

It would seem likely that if these two requirements were in place in NSW for Glenbrook and, if followed, would probably have prevented the accident from occurring.

In the Piper Alpha Inquiry it was revealed that a critical ten step Procedure required five additional steps, leaving aside that non-compliance with the ten steps was already high.

How to mitigate the risk

In my training in the early 1980s I was constantly asked by my mentor, Bob Thorpe, a highly respected Divisional Inspector two questions. 'What does the Procedure say' and 'why is it written like that?' It wasn't just being able to repeat the R&P it was about being able to understand its specific intent. He advised to read one R&P per day, something I did for many years, gradually building up my knowledge and understanding. It enabled me to debate with staff, supervisors and later, even the 'lawyers'.

In the 1980s in British Rail almost all managers had a reasonable knowledge of the Rules certainly in the O&M fields. Perhaps the old militaristic ways of those days were responsible for the lack of training in what management's responsibilities were and how we were expected to identify and manage risks. A time of high knowledge but perhaps a lack of a sophisticated understanding of their responsibilities.

By contrast in the 2020s it has become quite common to have multiple layers of managers with little or no knowledge. I can't imagine that happens in O&M in oil and gas or mining. That loss of knowledge has not been replaced by a more professional, skilled management.

This creates a two-railway syndrome within the management teams where seasoned experts are becoming the minority in senior management teams. An undesirable hollowing out has occurred, leaving aside the inability to analyse data, investigate or understand the concepts of the 'Swiss Cheese' model or Loss Control theory.

Ownership of each R&P

In SBS Transit Rail, unlike any other integrated Rail O&M company I am aware of, we did not have the traditional owner/writer Section for the R&P but gave the ownership of the R&P to the main user of that R&P, a Departmental Head. After all, they were responsible for ensuring that there was a safe and efficient method of work. It concentrated the mind.

A safety manager has the responsibility for overseeing the Modification Control Process, for ensuring that any changes did not inadvertently open up new 'holes'.

There was something quite neat and joined up in SBS Transit Rail's approach. Escaping the 'lawyers' and passing the ownership onto the Line Manager helps to clarify the roles and is also in line with the legal requirements of the Departmental Manager in respect to the provision of a safe system of work, competence, monitoring etc.

Seven: R&P&WI not monitored

The risk

The requirement of the Health and Safety legislation is that employers must take all practical steps to identify and mitigate risk to ALARP or SFAIRP in Rail in Australia.

The common risk is that staff do not strictly follow the R&P&WI but adopt informal methods of work. Ensuring that this does not occur is a Line Management responsibility from both a practical and a legal perspective, particularly Supervisors who have a critical role in reinforcing knowledge, enhancing understanding and promoting good practice.

The Safety Department are not responsible for doing the Line Managers' job. Safety Heads are responsible for providing the three As: Advice, Analysis and Audit – the Audit includes checking to see if Line Managers are complying with their obligations.

At the Inquiry into the Clapham Junction Train Crash in December 1988 it was revealed that nobody had checked, or could reference any check on the technician's work. This finding raised a consciousness in Operations about our own obligations around monitoring all staff in a systematic way.

In the Piper Alpha Inquiry it was found that the senior management were easily satisfied that the laid down governance arrangements were working well and effectively. A frequent problem in Rail O&M management.

How to mitigate the risk

While regimes to observe all staff during normal work is essential, on its own it has been shown to be insufficient. In the eighth risk, the next section the challenge of at-risk people and at-risk procedures is considered but experience has shown that with 'in hindsight', managers already had a strong sense that person X or procedure Y was a problem. Not to have acted is not defensible – it is denial behaviour, reckless.

As seen in the Inquiry into the Mid Staffordshire Health Authority in the UK in 2013, where managers used the terms 'in hindsight', or 'with the benefit of hindsight' 378 times, the risks were well known. Same for the data for the Nimrod crash in 2006 and for the reliability challenges in Southern Region of BR in 1986, reliability challenges in SBS Transit Rail in 2015 – the information was there. The Senior Management, in each case were too easily satisfied.

Eight: No practice of degraded and emergency procedures resulting in sub conscious incompetence.

The first time it occurred to me that most of our people were probably trained but incompetent was in 1990 when challenged over the competence of an InterCity train driver based in Swansea.

He had failed to quickly and smoothly handle a train breakdown just outside London on an evening peak service to South Wales. The Regional Train Crew Officer wanted him disciplined because the records showed that the driver had been trained to handle that fault. In 1976! Even though there was no record of that fault ever occurring on these trains.

The Regional Manager had done his A Levels in 1976 and obtained an A grade in chemistry. I suggested that while we waited to see the driver that he sit in the office and re-sit his chemistry A level paper and that if he obtained an A grade I would discipline the driver.

He told me that I was being ridiculous. "You started it", I replied.

The seed was sown. As O&M Managers we should have a system to ensure that the staff are not only trained and assesses as competent but that they should remain in a state of high readiness.

When we managed the start-up of the North East Line in Singapore in 2003 we put in place arrangements to try to achieve this.

The risk

There are three types of work and related R&P&WI:

- Daily tasks where on the job monitoring and observation is an effective competence assessment tool.
- Degraded mode where the need to conduct the task is infrequent but reasonably predictable in their occurrence.
- Emergency mode where the community expectation is that the response will be safe and quick but that, even over a 40-year career, it is unlikely that the knowledge will ever be applied.

This risk is concerned with how to 'take all reasonable steps' to ensure that staff are not only competent, in that they have been trained, but that they must remain competent and be in a state of high readiness to apply their knowledge. Being trained is not enough. Staff, including managers, must be 'combat ready'.

The graph below shows what happens to real competence and confidence levels after day one if there is not an active Competence Assurance Regime in place to build confidence and competence over time to enable them to grow rather than fall.

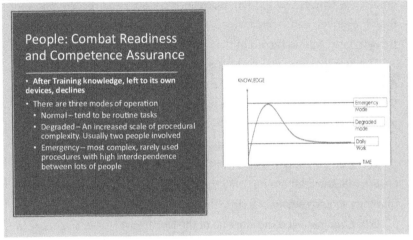

How to mitigate the risk

While on the job monitoring deals with the daily tasks it does not deal with the others.

A good practice regime has a drill, practice and assessment regime for all Operations staff. Depending upon the length of service and previous assessments there should be different frequencies.

The frequency should be aimed at building a sense of conscious competence for many degraded modes. Examples include:

- A GoA4 Metro operator, having on-train staff conduct a 12 car push out correctly eight times in the first two years, then twice in year three before reverting to an annual demonstration and assessment.

- Similarly, manual operation of lifts to enable stuck passengers to be safely and quickly removed weekly for eight weeks then monthly for 12 months before resorting to a half yearly assessment.
- Assessment of the roles and duties during an emergency station evacuation due to fire/explosion six times in years one and two.

The drills, exercises and assessments should be carried out during normal operating hours and conducted by the supervisors with spot checks of assessed staff and checks regarding recent drills etc by junior managers. Typically, a member of the Operations Group would be expected to be assessed aspect of their knowledge and understanding each fortnight.

The investigation into the Kings Cross Fire in London in 1987 provides a good example of not being 'combat ready'. It was discovered that London Underground did not have a workable Emergency Management Plan for the station, nor sufficient people or equipment available to implement one, nor were the people available in a state of high readiness to implement it.

Of the 11 O&M Operators I have working knowledge of since 2011 nine of whom have busy city centre underground stations, only three had the following:

- An emergency management plan that was understood to be workable.
- Sufficient staff and equipment on duty to be able to implement the Plan.
- Only two had arrangements to ensure that staff are in a state of high readiness - yet they all stated that safety was their first priority!

In lower performing Rail organisations, it is common for such checks to be conducted less than annually. The reliability of these Operators is generally poor particularly during degraded modes. Not surprising really yet their management still claim to put safety and customer interests as top priorities.

As Du Pont would say, you get the performance that you demonstrate that you want. I agree.

Nine: At risk Procedures exist

<u>The risk</u>

That there are some Procedures where many staff have an incorrect understanding of the requirement.

In ScotRail in 1992 Brian Panton, the Train Drivers Manager at Edinburgh found a way of discovering high non understood Procedures, at no cost by having all train drivers in Edinburgh asked two questions per months. Patterns emerged.

There were some questions that nearly all the drivers got wrong while there were many that they all got right. At risk Procedures had been identified. He took a proactive, systematic identification of risk. The at-risk Procedures were managed by a mixture of briefing or retraining in an attempt to close the identified gaps. This process also identified people whose understanding was generally much worse than their peers, at risk People.

In the table below an X indicates an incorrect answer to a question.

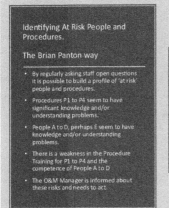

Identifying At Risk People and Procedures.

The Brian Panton way

- By regularly asking staff open questions it is possible to build a profile of 'at risk' people and procedures.
- Procedures P1 to P4 seem to have significant knowledge and/or understanding problems.
- People A to D, perhaps E seem to have knowledge and/or understanding problems.
- There is a weakness in the Procedure Training for P1 to P4 and the competence of People A to D
- The O&M Manager is informed about these risks and needs to act.

Procedures / People	P1	P2	P3	P4	P5	P6	P7	P8	P9	P10
A	X	X	X	X	X		X	X		
B	X	X	X	X		X	X		X	
C	X	X			X			X		X
D	X	X	X	X	X	X				
E	X	X	X	X						
F	X	X								
G	X		X							
H		X	X							X
I	X	X		X						
J	X	X	X							
K		X						X		

<u>How to mitigate the risk</u>

On SBS Transit Rail's Downtown Line start-up, by using this approach on the 80 or so Rules and Procedures that were assessed for approximately 140 people approximately 20 Procedures had a fail rate in excess of 50%. It led to a very focused briefing and reassessment programme.

Without this approach we would never have known except, perhaps, by hindsight.

In hindsight I would want to brief and/or retrain Control Room staff when at-risk Procedures are identified particularly if they relate to degraded or emergency modes to ensure that more attention is paid to instructions to staff.

Ten: Managing changes of the R&P

The risk

That changes to the R&P&WI are not well known or understood by the staff who need to change their working methods.

If the changes are not well known and understood there is a strong likelihood that non-compliance will be high and that 'holes' will open up. Eventually it would result in a two-railway syndrome becoming established.

How to mitigate the risk

Once a change has been approved there is a need to update all the relevant documentation and promulgate the changes to those affected. This is all tracked through the Modification Change Process and should include:

- o That any training and assessment material is updated.
- o That the staff are made aware of the change.

A good practice is to recognise that there are three categories of change based on risk.

- • Category A was minor, and changes could be shared at shift briefings.
- • Category B change was significant and required formal briefing to all affected staff before the change was made.
- • Category C change was major and required retraining before the change was made.

In each case, following the change there was a duty on supervisors to check compliance with the new requirement.

This may seem onerous but without it the 'as-is' state can become quite different to the documented state and the two-railway syndrome quickly emerges. It is up to the skill of the O&M Mangers to ensure that these steps are carried out.

What has this got to do with reliability?

If the approach to the management of these risks is not managed systematically and with a high level of discipline and commitment the indirect causes that lead to major safety disasters and much lower than was possible reliability is likely.

In almost all of the Case Studies described in this book the warning signs were available for curious eyes which were subsequently ignored or perhaps unknown too until 'hindsight' popped up. In each case the sense of being easily satisfied was high but the causal acceptance of the norm was embedded.

The causes of both safety and reliability loss of control events increasingly appear to be common.

For reflection, the dilemma of Work Instructions

In the modern railway auditors often prevail and frequently insist that there should be work instructions for every task and evidence that they are complied with. This frequent insistence seems to be misguided but perhaps there are 'horses for courses'.

Normal mode

Normal mode work forms the basis of subconscious competence.

Some written procedures and WIs are required for the trainers and assessors to be able to instruct and assess the understanding of trainees but we can all undertake quite a lot of complex tasks without any written instructions. These include dressing ourselves, eating a meal, washing and swimming. We don't issue written instructions to our children as part of the parenting process.

Competence for normal mode is monitored through observation. I am not sure that issuing detailed work instructions for this type of work adds any value.

Degraded and Emergency Modes

Since degraded and emergency mode management inevitably requires intervention where the normal protection built into the design of assets and systems are going to be by-passed, documented procedures are required to ensure there is a consistency of action - those unintended consequences of incorrect actions are avoided and to ensure that the training and assessment will be effective.

In that sense there would appear to be a good basis for having written Instructions for the handling and repair of defective equipment and assets for maintainers and for operations staff who have to isolate and override normal designed protections.

For Preventative Maintenance activities having documented procedures is useful for training and assessments but for the daily task, the availability of checklists, particularly tolerance limits is useful. With an increasing use of Tablets for Maintenance staff recording of data is becoming easier using templates which often include tolerances and reminder notes.

Some, however, believe that all Corrective Maintenance activities require Work Instructions. The problem with this is that the number of scenarios is endless. For example, Work Instructions for all scenarios for Control Centre management. Who would write and read them? Would staff remember them and be able to apply them correctly?

For OCC staff training and assessment using Adult Learning Principles builds understanding and enables people to apply their underpinning knowledge correctly. This has been shown to be an effective part of the risk management strategy.

Competence in the competence of Operations staff should be monitored through ongoing assessment and sample checking of knowledge, understanding and performance. If a person makes more errors than colleagues perhaps that person is an 'at-risk' person or there is an 'at-risk' procedure. Writing more Work Instructions is unlikely to help in either case. (I am aware of one major but poor performing O&M Operator who does not conduct any Control Room assessments after their initial training and assessment, not ever. Amazing)

The trainer, assessor, Departmental Manger and supervisor have a role to play in minimising the likelihood of errors being made with degraded mode procedures although Procedures are required for training and monitoring purposes.

For Emergency modes these rarely applied, multi-party procedures need documentation and frequent checking of understanding to maintain 'combat readiness'.

The danger of writing more and more instructions appear to be a response to wanting to have an individual to blame (very British Rail in the 1980s) rather than understanding that there are complex risks which require a nuanced management response.

Writing more and more instructions brings with it many obligations of practicality, compliance and the challenge of being sufficiently comprehensive. A risk of closing one perceived risk but replacing it with others.

People: Competence and confidence: Nine Common Risks

I *have identified nine common risks regarding competence, which re-*
quires the same rigor, discipline and associated management processes
and systems to prevent the known sources of weakness from opening
up and resulting in unplanned, unwanted, unexpected loss of control events.

This section attempts to share insights into the 'People risks' and how they
can be well mitigated by Line Managers.

While the two previous sections look at the approach to managing Assets and Procedures it all comes together with people, their competence, their confidence, their attitude and how this fits around the Company's appetite for excellence.

While an earlier section discusses the cultural norms and recognises the predominance of the Administrative culture where most people are going through the motions, sustainable high performance requires a well-structured, disciplined framework and timetable of activities, a Management System including monitoring of compliance and follow up.

Without such a System maintaining a sustainable high-performance culture is impossible.

Experience shows that there are some common sources of risk with the competence and confidence of staff and Contractors.

The MacDonald's scenario applies here. It doesn't matter where you are in the world the products taste and characteristics are consistent. They have well established processes and systems coupled with good discipline.

While there is a technical complexity in the Assets and Systems and in creating Rules, Procedures and Work Instructions I believe it is this human aspect where the greatest challenge lies.

This section attempts to identify those risks and proposes mitigation measures.

The Nine Risks

We know the following is almost certainly the case:
- To know about vulnerability and risks and to take action is a legal requirement. For O&M Managers 'not knowing' is not an excuse
- Selecting the right people is often ad hoc resulting in the wrong person being selected for the job.
- Initial Training and Assessment highlights areas of incompetence which needs examination and follow up even if passmarks have been met.
- A recognition of the Probationary (P) Plate period and people forgetting what they have been taught and do not regularly practice.
- That newly trained staff adopt local practices in breach of Procedures and Work Instructions in line with their more experienced colleagues.
- That staff forget much of their initial training and become subconsciously incompetent.
- There are known 'at risk' people.
- The failure for staff to reach a common understanding of who is going to do what and when in degraded operations has contributed to numerous loss of control incidents during my career.
- Situational Awareness needs to be high at the high-risk times

One: The Management Obligations: To know and to act. Not knowing is not an excuse.

The Risk

How common is it to know but not act? About at-risk people, at-risk assets, at-risk procedures, at-risk supervisors and at-risk managers, reliability risks? Very common. It is staring you in the face if you want to see. The same as reliability risks.

Many managers and supervisors turn a blind eye to causal factors if you do too. Visible leadership sets the tone and the mood. We know this, both from analysis of the safety and reliability referenced in Part One of this book.

How to mitigate the risk

Managers need to be testing the mood and looking for weaknesses. Management Reviews, incident investigations, corridor meetings, site visits, staff discussions are mechanisms for 'sensing'. It is up to the senior managers in the first instance to demonstrate how they will deal with well-known bad practice by picking up the small leads. There are many informal opportunities to discover the real state of affairs and to follow it up. This demonstrates to those watching what the tolerance level is to bad practices, unreliability, unsafety, unpreparedness for degraded and emergency events.

I once held a corridor discussion with a shift manager from an Operations Control Centre, OCC, and asked how things were going and how I might be able to help with any frustrations in the workplace. Imagine my surprise when he replied, 'If I tell you, will you promise not to name me?' I was told about the multiple repeats of many sub system failures that left the Line on the brink of significant unreliability every day. It led to the change in the three times weekly Fault and Delay (F&D) meeting referred to earlier. Once the senior management showed some interest, discipline and focus performance improved markedly.

In another Operator the now retired head of Rolling Stock told me that the improved performance on a competitors Line had embarrassed him, so he began to attend the regular F&D meetings on his railway again, something he had not done for many years and found that there were many opportunities to improve asset performance which they implemented. Reliability quickly improved a lot. All the senior management had to do was look. The evidence was there all the time.

Managers do have to do this 'sensing' or follow up on discovered events, everybody will watch and act accordingly. I have never encountered any push back from managers or supervisors when taking action on previously tolerated events and behaviours.

The following examples highlight examples where not knowing would have been part of the excuse. It illustrates a broader cultural problem of not wanting to know and the importance of confronting issues where the 'staff are all watching' to see how you react, or not as is often the case.

In Sydney in 1998 I checked up on fire and evacuation training of staff at the busy underground stations during my walkabouts on Thursday mornings, something I diaried every week. I discovered that they had not been trained on fire and evacuation requirements, even though the senior management told me that they had been. I had been CEO for two weeks and it was 11 years after the Kings Cross fire and I was interested to know the state of readiness. It was very low.

Also, in Sydney in 1998, during my Thursday walkabouts with local managers, I asked them about their last lost time injury, particularly the length of absence and what actions had been taken to prevent a recurrence. Not one manger was able to answer the questions but expressed the view that safety was their first priority.

Whether you like it or not the staff are watching you. If you 'walk past' the risk everybody will notice.

In 1985 as a new Traffic Manager I was informed about the Ipswich Station shunters sickness roster where one of the team would phone in sick allowing another to work their rest day. All the staff and supervisors knew about the longstanding problem, but they watched me. What is his tolerance level on this?

The Ipswich supervisors and staff wanted me to act and wondered if I would since the previous management had not acted. They followed the leader and adopted the to the tone. We stopped the sick roster together. It was a matter of self respect.

Similarly in 1989 we confronted the drinking on duty in Swansea. The supervisors and the staff all knew who the drinkers were. As at Ipswich, the supervisors and managers watched. What is his tolerance level on this? They followed the leader and adopted the to the tone. Again, we stopped it, together.

On safety, reliability, competence assurance, environmental requirements, emergency readiness it was always the same. The senior staff are watching and will adjust accordingly.

The problems are almost always well-known, same as the reliability vulnerabilities. To me, not acting, particularly when supervisors and experienced staff knew and had spoken about a problem was never an option. I had an obligation to act, as a matter of self-respect.

Two: Selecting the right people is often ad hoc resulting in the wrong person for the wrong job. Insufficiently qualified and experienced for the task at hand.

The risk

Unqualified, inexperienced managers and supervisors are sometimes appointed to key roles. It could be called appointing the wrong 'horse for the course'.

How to mitigate the risk

For senior managers see Part One

For Train Drivers and Train Controllers, for example, studies have been conducted that reveal that different personality types suit different work environments much better than others.

Psychometric testing for these key roles has been shown to assist with selection of the right type of people for these jobs.

In ScotRail in 1993 an analysis of personality types for Train Drivers and Train Controllers revealed the following key findings:

- Good train drivers preferred working alone, repetitive tasks and following instructions.

- Good train Controllers, by contrast, prefer a team based environment, making decisions, coordinating actions in a dynamic, responsive environment.

As with senior managers, there are 'horses for courses'.

Three: Initial Training and Assessment highlights areas of incompetence which needs examination and follow up but are generally not so long as the pass mark has been met.

The risk

There are two key risks:

- Staff not being trained and assessed in line with proven Adult Learning Principles
- Staff are assessed as being competent but there are critical knowledge gaps, which the staff have signalled to the managers in the assessments.

How to mitigate the risk: Adult Learning Principles

Good practice shows that the approach to training and assessment was for understanding not recall. Having a good understanding of the matter in hand has been shown to be a better predictor of correct action compared to being able to recall the Rules and Procedures.

The initial assessments and the ongoing Competency Assurance drills and exercises assess understanding - not just whether people took the right steps. This strengthened the individuals' confidence and gave assurance to the senior managers about competence.

Closing the revealed knowledge or understanding gaps. During final assessments not many people score 100%. The question of whether to act on the identified knowledge/understanding gaps presents itself.

In ScotRail in 1991 during the Newton accident Public Inquiry it was revealed that the signalman, whose actions had nothing to do with the accident, had made the same errors in successive assessments – the mistakes were always the same. The question was asked; 'how many times does he have to tell you that he doesn't understand something before the management will act? His average scores had been well over 90% in successive assessments. It was a confronting question since there were over 2000 train drivers, signal-men and Control staff at the time. The challenge was not unreasonable on the basis of taking 'all reasonable steps'.

In SBS Transit Rail in 2002 we introduced a structured interview following final assessment with staff who had passed to discuss the questions that had been answered incorrectly in an attempt to close the gap. This was in re-sponse to the Newton Inquiry case.

With the vast majority of candidates the process was straightforward but it did reveal a small number of cases where the underpinning knowledge and understanding was badly flawed. Despite having passed the final assessments they were never appointed into Train Controller jobs.

The practice was still in place in 2017.

Four: A recognition of the Probationary P Plate period and that people soon forget what they have been taught and not practised.

The risk

That newly trained staff are trained and assessed but not really confident or competent. Without support and coaching they are likely to be uncertain and to make mistakes. Perhaps being categorised as 'not competent yet' would be a better reflection of the truth?

When I had been passed out in my Rules and Regulations in 1983 my Area Operations Manager advised me to consider myself as being on L plates – it was good advice. I was often very nervous and cautious when handling fore-seeable degraded failures for the first few times. I have come to call this pe-riod the P Plate period, adopting an Australian practice for new car drivers who have to go through a year of restricted conditions until they are deemed as competent.

Mitigating the risk: Maintaining Knowledge of rarely used Procedures and Readiness.

Good practice requires a drill, practice and assessment regime for all Op-erations staff. Depending upon the length of service and previous assess-ments there were different frequencies. The sense was that once a person

274 • SIMON LANE

had carried out a degraded or emergency task correctly ten times, they would be likely to apply that knowledge correctly when called upon to do so. The P Plate regime was developed to provide this.

The frequency was aimed at building a sense of conscious competence for degraded and emergency modes. For example, at SBS Transit Rail in 2004 conducting a 12 car push out correctly eight times in the first two years, then twice in year three before reverting to an annual demonstration and assessment, manually operation of lifts to enable stuck passengers to be safely and quickly removed weekly for eight weeks then monthly for 12 months before resorting to a half yearly assessment and assessment of the roles and duties during an emergency station evacuation due to fire/explosion six times in years one and two.

The objectives included building confidence and competence – both very important in degraded and emergency modes, building the role of the supervisor and junior manager in assessing competence, reinforcing knowledge and promoting good practice, bringing to life the obligation to 'take all reasonable steps to reduce the risk to as low as reasonably practical' and being 'combat ready' is a societal expectation in respect of degraded and emergency modes.

Five: Newly trained staff adopt local practices in breach of Procedures and Work Instructions but in line with their more experienced colleagues.

The risk

That staff move from the initial training and assessment period to the workplace where they discover that the common practice differs from the trained practice. This is a well known risk and is demonstrated in many of the case studies in this book. I refer to it as the two railway syndrome.

How to mitigate the risk.

Several control measures can reduce the likelihood of this occurring including frequent monitoring by senior departmental managers who have the knowledge and experience to identify when this is happening and the personal and legal responsibility to prevent it. The line manager has a legal responsibility for providing and ensuring that there is a safe system of work and that it is being complied with. Is this personal responsibility well known? It seems to vary a lot.

With new staff, monitoring should be at a much higher level than for experienced staff. Ideally this should be carried out by line supervisors as part of a support and assurance process.

Of course, if the supervisor is aware of and is allowing informal work methods then the problem is worse. If the supervisor allows informal methods of work their Line Manager must also be aware – it is how the rot spreads, like a cancer. This highlights the case studies from first risk in this section, if you see it you have to act. O&M Management is not for the faint hearted.

In SBS Transit Rail in 2003 there was an anonymous phone number where staff were invited to report improper practice. It was not unusual for staff members partners, parents of children to call to prevent identification of the source.

Six: That staff forget much of their training, particularly in respect to degraded and emergency readiness – a pathway to sub conscious incompetence.

See the section viii under R&P&WI; No practice of degraded and emergency Procedures resulting in sub conscious incompetence.

Seven: There are known 'At Risk' People

The risk

That there are staff, including supervisors and managers who fail the 'benefit of hindsight' test. Often, we know who they are but are uncertain how to deal with it.

In Swansea in 1989 there was a serious incident caused by driver error one day in West Wales. When a group of drivers asked who had been driving, upon hearing the name, they looked at each other and said 'if it was going to be anyone it was going to be him'. They knew who the at-risk drivers were themselves.

In SBS Transit Rail in 2015 a person acted both independently and incorrectly during a failure making recovery longer. Two weeks later two senior managers were overheard when discussing the case and said 'he has been breaking the rules for years, he always does whatever he wants'. A known but not treated at risk person.

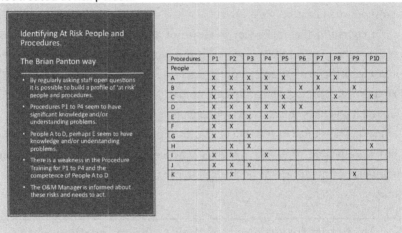

Identifying At Risk People and Procedures.

The Brian Panton way

- By regularly asking staff open questions it is possible to build a profile of 'at risk' people and procedures.
- Procedures P1 to P4 seem to have significant knowledge and/or understanding problems.
- People A to D, perhaps E seem to have knowledge and/or understanding problems.
- There is a weakness in the Procedure Training for P1 to P4 and the competence of People A to D
- The O&M Manager is informed about these risks and needs to act.

Procedures	P1	P2	P3	P4	P5	P6	P7	P8	P9	P10
People										
A	X	X	X	X	X		X	X		
B	X	X	X	X		X	X		X	
C	X	X			X			X		X
D	X	X	X	X	X	X				
E	X	X	X	X						
F	X	X								
G	X		X							
H		X	X							X
I	X	X		X						
J	X	X	X							
K		X							X	

In ScotRail in 1992 Brian Panton not only identified at-risk procedures but also at-risk people, those whose failure rate was much higher than his colleagues. With the Downtown Line in Singapore in 2016, of the 140 staff approximately 20% had a failure rate over 40%, despite having passed final assessments. In both cases the Management had become informed and could act. Using Brian Panton's approach cost nothing.

How to mitigate the risk

- At-risk Junior Staff

SBS Transit Rail adopted the Brian Panton process to identified at-risk people as well as at-risk procedures. It was used on both the North East and Downtown Lines revealing both at risk People and Procedures but with a slight difference.

Whereas Brian had questions asked monthly, in SBS Transit they were asked either weekly or fortnightly at different times but the questions were distributed in advance – the objective was to raise knowledge and confidence. At-risk people and procedures still revealed themselves.

- At-Risk Supervisors and Managers

Through investigations and discussions, it came to light that there were supervisors and managers whose attitude to compliance was, at best, poor. These at-risk people were relatively well known but senior management had taken no action.

As part of a programme to learn more about these people it was found on re-examination that their knowledge as well as their attitude was poor too.

What worked?

In almost all cases when the at-risk people had been interviewed and had learned that they had a much higher failure rate than their peers the vast majority made a big effort to improve. They were almost all determined to get off the 'watch list'.

There were also cases when there was no improvement and a tighter performance management regime was applied which resulted in some people leaving the business, mostly of their own accord.

The cultural impact

There were many benefits with improved focus and accountability for supervisors to improve their people's scores.

The staff knew they would be questioned and marked and the supervisors' role as assessors and enforcers, promoters of knowledge and understanding and good practice helped to cement them in as being responsible for bringing risk-identification and emergency readiness to life for front line staff.

This also assisted to enhance their role as sources of information about the business in a more general sense which assisted with organisational alignment. As with the almost everything else it required a disciplined and regular rhythm.

My reflections on this is that while managers usually have reassessment plans for front line workers it is much less common for supervisors and managers - people who can do a great deal of damage to the general culture particularly when they are well known (often the case) and seen to be beyond reproach.

In hindsight I think that having identified a person as being at-risk they should be told and a discussion about why be had. I believe that most people would respond to this positively.

Each at-risk person, as with an at-risk procedure require more attention and more monitoring and assessment. Managers are required, under the Health and Safety Acts, to take all reasonable steps to mitigate an identified risk.

Eight: The failure for staff to reach a common understanding in degraded operations.

The risk

The failure to reach a common understanding between people, typically signallers or train controllers with outside staff, during degraded operations has contributed to numerous loss of control incidents during my career.

Over the years the failure for staff to follow the laid down procedures has contributed to many incidents, particularly at Glenbrook where communications were particularly slack.

Why is non-compliance so high in so many regimes that I am aware of in UK, Australia and Singapore? The airlines don't seem to have this problem. The non-compliance is known and passively allowed by non-action in many railways despite the evidence of the risk.

As Du Pont say, you get the level of safety, performance, compliance etc that you demonstrate that you want. It certainly applies here.

How to mitigate the risk

In high performing O&M companies there is a regime of reviewing and reporting the level of strict compliance for each person with more attention and higher frequency for poor performers and subsequent follow up action. Deliberate non-compliance is treated as gross misconduct after two breaches.

Nine: Situational Awareness needs to be high at the high-risk times.

The risk

Situational awareness requires people to take extra care when required. This recognises that people cannot maintain high readiness and hyper vigilance all the time otherwise it would be called normal.

In Railways, during degraded operations when some of the normal control measures or organisational defences are not in place, when the consequences of error are raised, more care and attention is required. This is particularly true in Control Centres, Signal boxes and for first line responders whether they are operational or maintenance staff.

The trouble with unreliable railways is that working in degraded mode can become so common that the sense of requiring taking additional care becomes degraded, it has been normalised and a level of complacency sets in..

There is a need for high attention and care is when the normal control measures are not in place. Logical isn't it. I was never taught this, but I think it is a key point, particularly around clear communication protocols.

In Margam, Port Talbot, Wales in January 1991 we had a visit from a senior manager from Du Pont to observe the Area's regular Health and Safety Forum which had been very successful in bringing together staff interests and concerns with local managers. A great deal had been achieved over an 18 month period but there were still unresolved issues.

The staff asked Mr Du Pont about the known slippery underfoot conditions in an are of the depot which they had been asking to be resolved, a difficult task because of the leaky, old locomotives. They, and I, were expecting Mr Du Pont to support them but he didn't.

He asked about the road conditions and their driving style along he windy, narrow approach road to the depot on a clear, dry summer morning then their approach on a cold, icy, dark winter morning. They answered that the drove quite differently.

He explained that this was situational awareness in action and therefore, since they knew that the underfoot conditions in a specific area of the depot were slippery it was reasonable for them to treat it accordingly.

Since then, I have often reflected on the concept of reasonable-ness, a term used in the Health and Safety legislation. I came to be-lieve that it is unreasonable for staff to be asked to be on high alert at all times but reasonable to do so when the circumstances were much riskier.

I also came to realise that during degraded and/or emergency modes staff were being asked to work without some of the designed protections from being in place. This required staff to take much more care.

How to mitigate the risk

In SBS Transit Operations in 2016 after discussions with all the senior man-agers following on from a quarterly strategic review the staff were briefed about the concept of Situational Awareness.

It was a challenging concept for many who believed being on high alert was always required. We concluded that being vigilant was different from being on high alert. When we drive our cars we are expected to be highly vigilant but that under specific circumstances much more care is required, including slowing down etc.

Increasing awareness of Situational Awareness was important in the reliability improvement drive. Operations staff who led service recovery efforts became used to the idea of having to be much more careful, not necessarily slower, when taking actions when some of the designed safety features were being bi-passed.

An Aside: The Ironies and Risks of Advanced Automation

In the more advanced Systems, such as with the fully driverless Metro systems, many of the previous manual tasks and decision making have been removed. While this has great performance benefits it has undesirable side effects particularly in respect to a lack of practical knowledge and a sense of complacency.

Lisanne Bainbridge, a cognitive psychologist published a Research paper entitled 'The Ironies of Automation' in 1983, explains that Automation leaves the tasks that the designer could not design out, the most complex tasks, and that a reliable automatic system denies the opportunity to practice the skills that will be called upon in an emergency.

She also highlights that as a result of the lack of normal hands-on practice and the high engineering sophistication and redundancies the Operator inadvertently forgets 'to be afraid'.

It is essential that skills, particularly those associated with degraded and emergency modes need to be practised continuously in order to preserve them and that the staff need to be made and kept aware that when they act in such circumstances, they are overriding the designed in risk control barriers.

It brings to bear the importance of Situational Awareness, an essential requirement to avoid unintended consequences, the need to understand the need to be on alert when things are not normal.

CHAPTER TWENTY FIVE

Modification Control: The six required areas of focus

If one accepts James Reason's Swiss Cheese theory and that loss of control events occur when the organisational barriers put in place to avoid loss of control events have failed - usually with several 'holes' lining up then the importance of Modification Control reveals itself.

Every time a 'barrier of risk control' is changed it is important to ensure that no other barriers are weakened or holes opened up as an unintended consequence.

Modification Control is not an administrative process. It requires discipline and that skeptical mindset.

This Part Five of the book has tried to highlight the challenges of maintaining healthy and complete interfaces between the moving parts of the three segments identified in the Operator's Challenge:

1: Assets and Systems,

2: Operating Rules, Procedures and Work Instructions

3: People and Competence

As the understanding of performance, condition and the consequential risks increases there is an almost continual need to keep adjusting the organisational defenses. The risk through this process is that as changes are introduced other 'holes' are inadvertently opened up.

Modification Control is the proven approach to handling this integration challenge.

Modification Control is not an administrative process.

It requires active, disciplined, vigilant management. If its importance is delegated to junior staff the relevant insignificance is signalled. It is a critical part of the System

Where should formal modification control be applied? Six areas

There are six areas where formal MCP control can help organisations mitigate against the creation of unintended risks as some control measures are changed. They are as follows:

- **Hard Barriers:**
    - Changes to asset and system configurations as the assets and systems risk profiles change. This requirement is normal and is often in place.
- **Soft Barriers**
    - Changes in Planned Maintenance Programmes as assets wear and tear.
        - Good practice suggests that having a two step method for preparing and recommending a change for the Director of Engineering to consider works best with the recommendation coming from an Asset Class owner and the approval coming from a Director with responsibility for all the engineering interfaces.
    - Changes in Rules Procedures & Work Instructions as methods of work are refined.
        - Good practice suggests that the practice outlined under the tenth Rules and Procedure risk is best practice.

- Changes in Selection, Training and Assessment to handle emerging Business Risks. I have never seen this approach in action, but I would recommend it.
    - A good practice would be to ensure that these changes do not inadvertently open up 'holes' elsewhere.
    - Changes should be carefully considered. As with changes to R&P using a checklist to ensure a series of checks are made would help maintain the structure and the independence of thought to prevent uncontrolled, unchecked changes from being made.
- Changes in ongoing Competence Assurance Plans to handle emerging Risks. I have never seen this approach in action, but I would recommend it.
    - A good practice would be to ensure that these changes do not inadvertently open up 'holes' elsewhere.
    - Changes should be carefully considered. As with changes to R&P using a checklist to ensure a series of checks are made would help maintain the structure and the independence of thought to prevent uncontrolled, unchecked changes from being made.
- Changes in Organisations Structures and Responsibility Trees can change. This emerged in British Rail in the reorganisation of British Rail in 1991 and again as part of the pre-privatisation disaggregation in 1994. Outside the UK I have not seen this discipline used.
    - Good practice suggests that all current accountabilities and responsibilities along with business rhythm/governance arrangements are listed with a disposition showing where they all migrate to.

- The required qualifications, skills and experience of the altered positions should be reviewed to ensure that the new organisation will be competent.

Is this all necessary?

My experience suggests that it is. While these requirements seem, at first glance to be arduous they have all emerged as required steps and checks to prevent unintended consequences - where holes are opened up through omission rather than deliberate action.

Like the systems engineering approach being required to systematically look for and close up 'holes' in the three segments Modification Control helps to avoid inadvertently opening up 'holes'.

Once the internal processes and systems are set up it becomes a matter of discipline to comply and the adoption of the sceptical mindset.

As Jim Collins wrote, 'disciplined thinking, disciplined people and disciplined action'.

What would James Reason have to say about all this?

'Keeping an organisation alive to the presence of risk is a great and important challenge.' In my opinion you can not do this without the supervisors and junior managers being deeply involved in identifying and mitigating risks.

'While there are lots of academic models home grown measures are most likely to be bought into, used and adjusted where necessary.' Their insights and suggestions are often not very sophisticated, but they can be very effective particularly where they feel personally committed which can come from involvement. Actually, I think not involving them is both a wasted opportunity and quite an insult to their knowledge and experience'.

I agree with Reason here. The risk mitigation measures in respect of the three segments are all home grown and were developed by supervisors and managers most familiar with the risks.

The Opportunity for achieving Excellence.

This Part Five has considered the risks which perhaps suggests that managing the three segments is all about risk identification and mitigation. While that is essential it is from a minimalist requirement alone.

The 'people' segment provides the opportunity to bring the various elements together to create an outcome much greater than the sum of the parts.

Reliability being sustained at more than double its RAMS design.

For the North East Line an assessment of the designed RAMS shows that an MKBF of 500k had been designed and commissioned. I learned this in 2018 after I had left SBS Transit Rail but it certainly puts into perspective the reliability in 2014 and 2015 when the MKBF was approximately 200k, the best ever and the best line in Singapore.

The MKBF in 2018 and 2019 was over 1.3 million and over 2.0 million in 2020 and 2021. The improved understanding and control of failures coupled with the improved operational response to delays had taken the performance well above its design.

Ambition, skill, discipline and multiple levels of organisational partnership

Perhaps it highlights the conservative commitments of the OEM in their design commitments, but it certainly demonstrates what can be achieved through a relentless, systematic identification and mitigation of risk, and the power of collaboration between Departments and between different levels within each Department – the five integrated levels of leadership, from the technicians and their supervisors to the Board.

The improved MKBF on SBS transit's Rail Lines was achieved with very little enhancement to the design.

Similarly, SMRT's Circle Line, SMRT's Bukit Panjang LRT and SBS Transit's Sengkang and Punggol LRT improved their MKBF in a way and to a level by

2021 that would have been regarded as both impossible an unsustainable in 2015.

Learning from others

Throughout my career I have been a 'bag lady of ideas', pinching and adapting them from wherever I could. I hope there are some here that will help you too.

In Singapore our visit to Taipei Metro in 2016 was particularly important. We learned and adopted their practice for attributing minutes of delay. In Taipei the first 3 minutes were being attributed to the engineer whose asset or system had failed with additional minutes being attributed to operation's people.

Prior to that, when there was a delay there was a sense that all the responsibility laid with the respective asset managers, in line with traditional practice of attributing cause to the primary failure alone.

What emerged was a more wholistic assessment of the incident. The operations people now shared responsibility for the consequences of the delay. In hindsight it was a critical learning on the MKBF improvement journey.

Internal Partnership

A great deal of the reliability improvement in SBS Transit Rail came from improved decision making and intervention following failures which typically reduced delays that might easily have exceeded 10 minutes in the past to under five minutes by 2017.

The shared responsibility on the engineers to reduce failures and for the operations people to reduce their impact established a single, shared, transparent dependency.

Success brought more determination and more success for the team. A bond between the operations and maintenance managers was an essential part of what Jim Collins calls the 'flywheel effect'.

In Sydney, for the Olympic Rail Task, that internal partnership also played a critical part of the story. Without that, I do not believe that it would have been nearly as successful.

If I was starting again, I would adopt this approach

Modification Control is not an administrative function. It requires significant focus since it is where the approval of changes in an O&M Organisation's barriers to prevent loss of control events are approved and their dissemination processes laid down.

While the need for tight modification is well known, but not necessarily well adhered too in respect of asset configuration it is much less well known and adhered to in the other five areas identified.

The sceptical mindset is important here since the danger of 'being easily satisfied' that things are in place and being adhered to lurk in the shadows.

PART FIVE: The complementary roles of the Owner and the O&M Manager

Over the last 20 years Franchising has become popular in the Rail Industry in the UK and Australia and in other countries such as Singapore a government agency has become more active in overseeing the management of the passenger rail O&M activities.

This section considers how the respective rights and obligations of the two partners, the System Owners and the O&M Managers best interact with each other.

Unfortunately for the industry, and for the proponents of franchising, Owners have become more prescriptive than ever envisaged which has blurred accountability and responsibility for poor performance.

John Nelson, in his book Losing Track, explains that over prescription by UK authorities has deprived the ability of UK Operators to significantly innovate for the benefit of the customer and the Rail Network since 2004 while in Australia the franchised Melbourne Operation has consistently performed worse than the government owned and managed NSW and Western Australian Train Companies from both a reliability and customer satisfaction basis yet in Melbourne's case over $1 bn of dividends has been paid to mostly overseas owned companies.

CHAPTER TWENTY SIX

The rights of the Owner

I observed this...over intrusive Control.

Owners being heavily involved with the minutiae of the O&M Manager's handling of all aspects of O&M including risk identification and mitigation plans making it very unclear where the final accountability sits.

Despite the stated Policy positions of the Governments who wanted to welcome the innovation and capability of the private sector then hold them to account for their delivery against output-based requirements the practice has been for Owners to treat the O&M as their O&M Contractor on a schedule of rates contract.

If Owners and/or State Agencies continue to be highly prescriptive and heavily involved in the 'how' which seems to involve a lot of 'man marking,' then perhaps the industry should revert to the State becoming the Operator again. At least the accountability is then clear and the doubling up of scarce expertise can stop.

Certainly in Australia, after 20 years of franchising in Victoria there is no apparent benefit of the franchising model. Performance is worse than in many comparable systems and the size of the Government Agencies are many times larger than under State Control.

A muddled adoption of Partnership

Having won O&M contracts the new fashion is for the Owner/State and the Operator to adopt a new partnership fudge. Why a fudge? The new arrangements are a far cry from tender documents which call for innovation with full accountability for developing and delivering a brand of excellence.

These new 'partnerships' allow the over sized Government Departments to micro manage the O&M Operator, despite having neither the qualifications, skills nor often the experience to hold the key posts, to the extent that the ensuing poor performance is seen as a joint exercise.

I have made two key observations in this regard. Firstly, when asked, contract managers in State Agencies have said that they could not countenance terminating the existing contract on performance grounds because of the 'unmanageable gap' created in terms of who would take over in the short term.

Secondly, that when new O&M Operators are appointed, except in the most bizarre circumstances, only the CEO, CFO and perhaps Corporate Comms Director need to be replaced in the fist instance. The rest of the people carry on until things get changed, or not.

An apparent exception to this is in some of the UK franchises where whole management teams get replaced on franchises changing hands. More craziness. Transition periods for newly appointed senior managers is a tricky process unless the circumstances are so dire that immediate drastic action is required. Changing out whole teams creates no sense of continuity and inevitably destabilizes any disciplined processes and systems which are the glue that enables excellence to prevail.

The industry would do better if the Owner/State concentrated on the 'what' and encouraged the Operator to develop ideas and proposals to achieve 'remarkable' outcomes. In the UK the transformation of the Chiltern Lines came about through the innovation, courage and insight shown by Adrian Shooter and a State that allowed his team to flourish leaving a wonderful legacy of a highly improved railway.

In the post Hatfield era, it is a shame that South West Trains was prevented from bringing a highly visionary proposal to fruition on both the inner London Windsor Lines and the South West Main Line to Bournemouth. As

John Nelson reported in his book Losing Track, the SWT proposal to convert the Windsor Line operation to 10/12 cars in four years took Network Rail a decade.

In Australia there are no examples of Chiltern type comparison except perhaps the Victorian State rejection of MTM's 2011 Strategic Operations Plan which would have brought much higher value and at lower cost than the Melbourne Metro project, more like the South West Trains post Hatfield proposal.

A Compromised Franchisee

The nature of the relatively short contracts in Suburban O&M Contacts and even in longer term PPP arrangements creates a conflict between the Guiding Principles, particularly in respect of being a long-term steward for the railway, optimising the life cycle costs and even building the capability and capacity of people with the commercial objectives of the O&M Companies.

Under Australian Corporations Law the Boards of Companies have an obligation to act in the interests of the shareholders. Consequently, when faced with choices as to the extent to which Contractors are driven by the Guiding Principles versus the opportunity to improve or maintain their profit margin it is both likely and perfectly acceptable that they take the profit.

This puts the onus on the owner/regulator in terms of the Contracts. Since the O&M Contractor has legitimate objectives which are conflict with the Guiding Principles it is up to the Owner, in their contacts, capability and decision making to uphold the long-term stewardship, the long term cost optimisation and capability development.

Where this is not done the whole industry is weakened. In Singapore, it is a poorly kept secret that SMRT pursued profit maximization between 2002 and 2011 by which time many of the assets and systems had deteriorated in condition and reliability which led to a crisis regarding condition and performance. Managers became conditioned to not ask for the required resources. From 2002 when SMRT and MTR in Hong Kong were seen as being on a similar trajectory, to 2012 when MTR were world leading in asset management and operational performance SMRT had become a distant cousin.

In Australia, with MTM in Melbourne and MTS in Sydney, performance is much lower than many other comparable Systems. The Owning Authorities have allowed this to occur. The Contractors have legitimate objectives which may well not be in line with the long-term stewardship of the respective systems.

The outcomes reflect Du Pont's saying that 'one gets what one demonstrates that it wants'.

In Singapore, SBS Transit and ComfortDelgro did not pursue a short term profit maximization mantra, perhaps recognising the need to meet the Social Contract obligation between private sector and Government. The Singaporean Government or its agencies had no shares in either SBS Transit of ComfortDelGro in the time when I worked for them.

The obligations of the Social Contract, which balances short term profits against the Guiding Principles need to be picked up by the Owner in commercial contracts.

My own reflection on the SBS Transit Rail improvement from delays over 5 minutes every three weeks or so to once or twice per year required an injection of costs to shift from a reactive to proactive culture but the value of this improved reliability and the removal of so much 'noise' associated with the reduction in loss of control events provides both vale and savings. Without the Minister's public call for improvement the short term increase in costs required may not have been forthcoming. The Owner has to set the tone. Profit driven Corporations have no incentive to do this on their own.

A lack of accountability

In the UK and Australia there is little evidence of their being a clear delineation of the role and responsibilities of the Owner and the O&M Manager with 'man marking' and interference of the O&M Manager being a common feature of the various regimes.

In Melbourne, for example, pre franchising the Dept of Transport had approximately 25 people which included managers of private bus contracts. By 2018 this 25 had increased to over 1200.

This man marking blurs the lines of responsibility and accountability which is a recipe for mediocre performance at best.

An acceptance of poor performance by franchisees

In the UK has a franchisee lost its contract since Connex on the South Eastern franchise in the late 1990s due to poor performance? Many have ended due to commercial problems but not due to poor delivery. Even the Thameslink debacle in 2018 was tolerated.

In Melbourne, Australia the performance of Connex between 2004 and 2009, and MTM after 2015 were well below the earlier achievements of the Public Transport Corporation Met Trains Business Unit of the mid to late 1990s yet, as in the UK, the performance was tolerated.

In Sydney, the reliability of the privately owned MTS is approximately 50k in terms of MKBF compared to over 2 million in Singapore.

When asked, the Government's Contract Managers seem unprepared to consider contract termination. The Victoria and NSW Governments of the 1990s were much less tolerant of their own Managers.

I came to understand that, as a consequence

The full and intended benefits of franchising remain available but some key characteristics of the model seem to be required to ensure full and transparent accountability. They include a clear delineation of the role and responsibilities of the Owner and the O&M Manager

To be properly and systematically informed, requiring the O&M Manager to be able to meet the universal obligations of their role.

The O&M Manager should be able to demonstrate:

- An understanding of performance, capacity and condition at asset class and sub-system levels
- Documented foreseeable risks and challenges looking forward at defined periods – 3 months, 6 months, 12 months, 36 months, 72 months and 120 months.
- That the appropriate mitigation measures are in place to properly manage the risks and challenges

These Plans should document risk mitigation plans including resource requirements.

- Evidence that the accepted preventative action plans are being implemented in the required timeframe.
- Provide investigations reports and preventative action plans for notable loss of control events.

At its core a lack of clarity between the State and the O&M Operator has emerged. While the initial thinking was that the private sector would bring their genius to resolve all the long standing problems and that the Private Operator would be held accountable for all the outcomes over time the State have become increasingly intrusive.

It would help if the State Agency, usually the procurement Authority, were to document and publish the risk ownership profile. This should include:

- Those risks that the Private Operator will be expected to manage without recourse to the State Agency, unless a Directive was to be issued, in which case it should be published along with the rationale.
- Those risks that are to be jointly managed where both parties will collaborate.
- Those risks where the State will be the owner and will direct the O&M Manager.

Such clarity would assist both the Operator and the State Agency and clarify how the Guiding Principles are to be managed. If they are left in abeyance through omission then it is likely that the long-term stewardship, optimisation of life cycle costs and the building of capability of people will be compromised. As with SMRT's profit maximisation experiment, the consequential costs are very high, possibly much higher than the short-term profits made.

In Melbourne after 2009, as the Interim Chief Operating Officer of MTM, what became clear was that the State Agency wanted to be heavily involved in the ongoing decision making despite the Contract Terms making it clear that the decision making and the accountability laid solely with MTM.

By 2014 when the time for discussions on contract extension commenced the senior management of MTM were compromised. If they had worked to their contract conditions they would have been very unpopular with the State Agency who was considering their future.

It led to increasing intrusion, a blurring of accountability and a deterioration in performance. Who'd have thought it? Unaccountable, untrained State Agency managers directing the show. Where and who is guarding the Guiding Principles.

If I was starting again, I would adopt this approach

I would want to see much more clarity around the ownership of the risks and the accountabilities for the outcomes. If the State wants to involve itself in some matters then that should be made clear in the contract and adhered to.

I would want to see Owners and/or State Authorities stepping away from the 'how' so as to leave the Operator fully accountable for all the outcomes. This would make it simpler for poor performance to lead to more penalties including terminations of contracts while leaving the Operator to demonstrate their value.

In turn I would like to see Owners being much less tolerant of underperformance to encourage Operators to be rewarded for superior performance.

Conversely, I would like to see Operators focus on delivering outstanding performance across all areas rather than be focussed on compliance with minimum requirements which seems to have become the prevailing behaviour, aided by ever more prescriptive Owners and Government Agencies.

I would like to see the Owners as reviewers of the various Plans provided by the Operators, making choices of the preferred outcomes including provision of the required funding, if necessary.

CHAPTER TWENTY SEVEN

The obligations of the O&M Manager

The obligations are threefold.

Firstly, to be able to demonstrate their compliance with the Universal Obligations of the O&M Manager regarding the short to medium term performance.

Secondly to be able to demonstrate to the Owner the following, which in turn enables the Owner to be satisfied about performance and condition:

- That the asset maintainer satisfies themselves that the performance and condition of the assets are under control.
- That the KPIs enable the maintainer to systematically identify risks and challenges.
- That the KPIs enable the maintainer to track the mitigation of the risk closure and the effectiveness of the actions taken?

Thirdly, the provision of annual management plans provides the O&M Operator with the opportunity to provide the Owner/State with the following:

- An analysis of performance
- The identification of risks and challenges over the next two, five, ten and fifteen years
- Costed options on how these risks and challenges could be met with a recommended pathway for the Owner to consider.

This approach enables the O&M Operator to demonstrate their skill, expertise and experience for the Owner to benefit from. They do not need to do a parallel process. They are usually unqualified to do so.

While looking fifteen years ahead is almost certainly beyond the Operator's contract it does provide a base line assessment of the years ahead. The Owner needs this since many short term decisions are best made understanding the medium to long term perspective.

After living away from the UK for over a decade and reading about the surge in ridership and investment, particularly in Rolling Stock I was shocked to see the new trains for inner London commuters having only two doors per carriage, the same as those built in the early 1980s. These trains replaced slam door rolling stock but the reduced door numbers caused dwell times to increase slowing down the network and, as a consequence, creating more 'noise' around network congestion.

Three doors per car would have provided more capacity but fewer seats. I can recall Network South East in London making its policy and service promises to the public in 1986 which included that passengers travelling over 20 minutes should be able to get a seat. It wasn't met in 1986 on inner suburban Lines so the promise was even further away in the mid 2000s. This is a case of using the past to guide investment decisions with a consequence for travellers on those lines until the 2040s. Quite avoidable. Even Melbourne had three door cars in the 1980s.

I came to understand that, as a consequence

It is important that the accountability for determining short to medium action plans are left with the O&M Managers, the accountable people.

History from the UK and Australia has shown that directives of actions by the Owner to the O&M Management, including the contents of action plans have had adverse effects including the following:

- A loss of accountability by the O&M Manager which seems to correlate with a the loss of high performance.
- An increase in the headcount of the Owners as they have adopted 'man marking' of the O&M Managers.
- The reduction in innovation - a key driver of the philosophy towards franchising and privatisation in the 1990s.

For longer term plans a longer term perspective is required - particularly for the key assets and systems including signalling, trains and power. This is looked at in detail in Part Six but the industry has a poor history of procuring new assets and systems without a long term end state to guide them resulting in decisions that come to be seen 'with the benefit of hindsight' as serious mistakes.

If I was starting again, I would adopt this approach

I would like to see Operators providing analysis of all key aspects of the O&M performance including safety, security, reliability, asset performance, competence assurance, emergency readiness etc. to the Owner/State.

These plans should comply with the Universal Obligations of O&M Management and include plans on how to deliver outstanding performance in each area. Let the Operator inform the Owner/State of their choices of outcomes and then let the O&M Manager be left to deliver those Plans.

This would enable the State to choose to fund alternative options in line with the Guiding Principles, or not but at least the choices would have been available instead of ignoring them through omission by both an O&M Contractor and the Owner/State.

Chapter Twenty Eight

Monitoring and Reporting

I have observed

R eports submitted, often on a monthly basis, that contain up to 350 pages of invalid data, analysis and miscellaneous reports that fail to meet any of the three universal obligations, specifically:

- No demonstration of performance or condition which despite the pages of detail fail to provide any valid analysis.
- No structured assessment of risks and challenges nor any status of the mitigation measures.
- No mitigation measures, even for the risks and challenges which may have been identified or assumed.

In short, these reports provide a fallacy of keeping the Owner/Regulator informed. These reports are not helpful to the Owner/Regulator but because of the lack of training in what valid analysis, risks and challenge identification and the consequential resourced, mitigation measures planned etc should look like, these reports are accepted.

Since many of the very long, poorly written reports are not read beyond the executive summary, claims that the Owner was informed about risks and challenges can be hidden within the depths of the content. Not very helpful to either party.

The lack of training is not only a feature and weakness of O&M Managers but includes Owners/Regulators too so the invalid, bad practices are allowed to continue, at best, in a state of learned helpfulness but perhaps providing a smokescreen for entrenched denial.

I came to understand as a consequence

Good practice demonstrates that a well structured, systematic reporting and monitoring system helps the Operators to demonstrate their performance against their Universal Obligations with a tier of reports. These should emerge from the Business Rhythm highlighted in Part One.

These reports should enable the Owner to be kept fully aware about performance and condition reducing the need for any man marking and detailed involvement in short term decision making.

As a consequence, the Operators are left fully accountable for risk identification with some shared accountability between Owner and the Operators depending on where the Owner funds the recommended risk mitigation plans.

A critical feature is the transparency of the analysis, risk identification and proposed measures.

Effective Reporting Arrangements might include the following:

- Monthly
  - A factual report regarding the last month
- Quarterly:
  - An assessment of performance, condition, risks and their mitigations looking forward 6 months. The analysis should be at sub system level for assets and operating sectors and use proven applied statistical techniques.
  - Are the risk mitigation plans on track? Is the risk profile improving or deteriorating?
- Annually: Maintenance and Work Plans
  - Includes a 15 year look ahead of Asset Condition
  - Recognises the need for a documented long term view of asset life.
  - Helps to capture the corporate history and understanding of expert perspectives before the experienced over 55's retire in the next decade.

A good practice non safety Performance reporting structure could look like this.

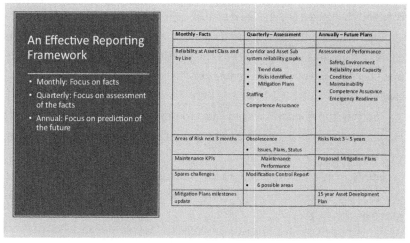

	Monthly - Facts	Quarterly – Assessment	Annually – Future Plans
An Effective Reporting Framework • Monthly: Focus on facts • Quarterly: Focus on assessment of the facts • Annual: Focus on prediction of the future	Reliability at Asset Class and by Line	Corridor and Asset Sub system reliability graphs • Trend data • Risks identified. • Mitigation Plans Staffing Competence Assurance	Assessment of Performance • Safety, Environment • Reliability and Capacity • Condition • Maintainability • Competence Assurance • Emergency Readiness
	Areas of Risk next 3 months	Obsolescence • Issues, Plans, Status	Risks Next 3 – 5 years
	Maintenance KPIs	Maintenance Performance	Proposed Mitigation Plans
	Spares challenges	Modification Control Report • 6 possible areas	
	Mitigation Plans milestones update		15 year Asset Development Plan

A Quarterly KPI reporting framework could look like this.

An effective Quarterly Reporting Framework • The focus is on understanding the frequency of leading loss of control indicators, the holes in the cheese which remain hidden to reports on outcomes only	Assets	R&P&WI	People	Operations
	Works order trend	Number reviewed and/or validated	Staff: Actual v Required	Errors and violations
	Work orders overdue	Reviews overdue	Initial Training and Assessment	No of degraded instances
	Rework/NFF	Instances of Non compliance found	Competence Assurance overdue	No of emergency instances
	Delayed waiting parts		CAP: Failed assessments	
	Cannibalised parts			
	Surprising events		Surprising events	Surprising events
	Issues of concern		Issues of concern	Issues of concern

If I was starting again, I would adopt this approach

A well developed hierarchy of Indicators fulfills five objectives.

Firstly, it provides the Owner/Regulator/State with information about the performance and condition of the assets and systems, the overall reliability and availability and a series of indicators where management control is of concern.

Secondly, with this hierarchy being provided by the Operator it enables them to demonstrate that they understand what is happening, where the risks and challenges are and their status.

Thirdly, without diluting the Operator's accountability for all the outcomes it highlights where the Owner may wish to obtain independent advice on a specific issue of concern and makes the need for man marking unnecessary.

Fourthly, the Annual Plans provide a context where the Owner/State may make a choice about what outcomes they wish to procure without interfering with the options development.

Fifthly, together this approach reduces the likelihood that the Owner/State become intrusive into the 'how' and the 'what' outside the annual Plan review process.

CHAPTER TWENTY NINE

The Duties of The Owner/Regulator

I observed low expectations

R ail O&M Franchises where the performance has been poor seemingly without penalty and, in many cases where franchise extension and renewal followed.

How is it that peak hour reliability in Melbourne was allowed to fall from a pre-Franchising minimum standard of 89% within five minutes to the low to mid 80 percentage for many years after the private sector took over? By 1987 over 93% was being achieved with a pathway to over 95% by 2000.

In Melbourne's case the Transport Minister of the day in 1994 made it clear, achieve peak reliability of 88% within five minutes or face removal. No such determination or statement has been made since 1999 franchising by a Minister or a Franchise Manager.

Who allowed this to be acceptable? The Owner/Regulator. Meanwhile in Sydney, Perth and Brisbane peak hour reliability well above 92% was completely normal pre Covid.

When there is strong evidence of Denial or Administrative cultures why do the Owner/Regulators appear to accept it?

In the UK since franchising became common after 1996, how many of the Train Operating Companies had their contracts terminated for poor operating performance? Any of them?

I observed top heavy bureaucracies

A shift to Ministerial interference in directing tactics which Ross Gittens referred to in the Sydney Morning Herald (020621) where Ministers 'are telling Bureaucrats that they don't need the advice, just their obedience' where politicians on both sides, captured by the mantra of small Government have gradually reduced the capability of the growing Public Service to do their job properly.

- Department of Transport, Victoria from 25 in 1996 to over 1000 in 2020.
- Department of Transport, NSW from 75 in 1996 to over 1000 in TfNSW today.

In the UK and Australian franchises, the Owners have adopted a practice of being highly intrusive and directive. As John Nelson, a former Senior Director in British Rail, wrote in his book Losing Track, An Insiders Story of British Rail Transformation from British Rail to the Present Day (2019), the interference and over prescription by Government Departments had removed any of the potential financial, capacity and service benefits of private sector involvement by 2004, within six years of the private operation of Passenger Services on the UK Network.

He particularly highlights two particular transformative projects offered by Stagecoach for South West Trains, London's biggest franchise, for completion within four years, both turned down by the Government who wanted to oversee their delivery itself. The first took ten years and the second has never been mentioned again.

I believe that there is an imperative

I would advise the Owner/State to keep out of the way of the Operator and how they do their O&M job.

On projects however, leaving aside the reporting on time and budget, the franchisee, as the project deliverer has a natural conflict between maximising its profit and doing the right thing for the long term operability and maintainability of the assets. The Owner/State needs to be informed and, ultimately the decision maker, about technical standards. The Owner/State needs to have the competence and expertise to exercise an informed judgement on these matters.

CHAPTER THIRTY

Private or Public Sector Management

I observed this

That the public sector management in the Australian systems in Perth, Sydney and Brisbane consistently delivered much higher quality outcomes than the private sector in Sydney and Melbourne over the past 30 years or so.

The continually creeping prescription seems to have diminished or even eliminated the expertise of the Operator. Certainly, the loss of accountability for all the outcomes on the Operator has led to a greater emphasis on compliance with shifting and often short-lived priorities of Politicians and Public Sector officials.

I came to understand that, as a consequence

The quality of the outcome reflected two key things

- The capability and appetite of the O&M Management team
- The clarity of the role and responsibilities of both parties in the contract

That the issue of private versus public sector management is inconclusive although the tolerance in British Rail, Melbourne and Sydney the late 1980s and 1990s. for poor performance appears to have been much lower than in those same jurisdictions than in the 2010s and early 2020s.

Melbourne

The key issue in the above article is the setting of targets and the threat of removal of those responsible if they weren't met.

During the 1996/97 financial year the peak reliability had risen to 92.4 despite four months of serious industrial action regarding the superannuation guarantees of a future corporatization, and an all-day reliability of 94.8 compared to 89.9% in 1993/94 and fewer than one cancellation in 200 services. There was the promise of peak reliability of 95% by 2001. The Public Sector delivering.

The franchised Operators have not got anywhere near the 1996/97 since the State/Operator partnership allowed the 95% peak hour performance to slip after 2003. In 2019 peak hour reliability in Melbourne was close to 84%. Why have the State Agencies and Ministers tolerated this?

Sydney Olympics Transport Task

A key feature of the Transport task was the bussing arrangements which included buses for the Public, the Media, the Athletes and the so called Olympic Family. This required hundreds of buses and their drivers to come to Sydney from across NSW and interstate. Ensuring that these temporary resources were well looked after and able to deliver their tasks in unfamiliar territory was significant.

The private bus Operators were asked to coordinate this.

After three very shaky days the Minister for the Olympics made a change and the Private Sector Managers were replaced by the Public Sector Sydney Busses Team. I will never forget the Minister explaining to the Media that the task had been too big and complex for the Private Sector managers. What a joy!

Reflections

High quality outcomes are delivered by skillful, experienced, disciplined teams which are well guided and empowered, irrespective of being employed by the Public or Private sectors.

The Private Sector Rail O&M Managers in the UK and Australia have been set low benchmarks and targets which are not often frequently missed but also tolerated. Who'd have thought it?

I later read this which reinforced my thinking and practice

In the Piper Alpha Inquiry Lord Cullen made two excellent points about the role of the Regulator, which apply equally to Network Owners in this context:

- Presumptive regulation or over detailed guidance may at times result in the overall objective actually being compromised.
- In aiming for compliance sight can be lost of the more realistic and overall intent that all reasonable steps should be taken.

If I was starting again, I would adopt this approach.

Ensure that the rights and responsibilities of the Owner and the O&M Manager are clear.

PART SIX: Railway Capacity Projects

After 2000, after many decades of falling or stable passenger ridership in Australia and the UK, rising ridership started to create significant capacity pressures on many networks.

The UK's Strategic Rail Authority led the way with the development of Rail Utilisation Strategies for all major routes which helped to shape strategies for enhancing the capacity of these routes in a systematic way. Unfortunately, the SRA did not survive another industry restructuring in 2006, and the discipline of the Rail Utilisation Strategy (RUS) planning process and the potential role that the private sector could play was lost after Hatfield, RailTrack etc as the Dept of Transport became increasingly prescriptive.

The RUS was not a perfect model, but it provided a good basis for going forward. Another key benefit of the RUS programme was that the documents were published allowing both enhanced understanding and critique.

In Australia, what generally emerged was politicians announcing expensive trophy projects which were supposed to solve long term problems, but which often had long term unintended consequences including a realisation that the objectives would not be met.

The term trophy projects is deliberately controversial but when these projects are based on unpublished Business Cases or even when they are, the obvious flaws in the Options Analysis and false benefit claims are used to increase benefits to the project. There are currently two Metro projects under development in Sydney with declared BCR ratios of 0.84 and 1.06 – hardly good use of public money, and one in Melbourne with a BCR of 1.1.

The Clearways programme in Sydney and the expansion of the Network in Perth are notable exceptions to this.

As an interested onlooker I developed an eight-step logic tree for helping to facilitate and/or assessing Major Rail projects. This logic tree framework has been used to assess major projects in several jurisdictions since 2008 when it was first used in a study of Sydney's 2040 Peak Hour requirement.

After using the Framework in seven countries evidence that politicians and/or senior civil servants are guilty of starting major project planning at step seven of eight is overwhelming – the early decision forces earlier steps to be forced through a reverse logic, often making decisions to reduce value and increase costs along the way.

Who benefits from this process? Many consultants. Nobody wants to call out the error of the chosen approach because of the long-term loss of business so 'independent advice' is used to shore up benefits even when a casual examination of the facts shows the 'advice to be erroneous. The case of NSW's Transport Asset Holding Entity illustrates a constant theme in the sector in Australia.

This section examines the Logic Tree and several case studies regarding Capacity Enhancement Projects.

It also examines the concept of Operational Readiness for major projects since the migration form the project phase seems to result in many problems in the start up phase with Bukit Panjang LRT in Singapore, Thameslink in UK in 2018 and Crossrail in UK highlighting common problems while the North East Line start-up in Singapore in 2002/03 provided a new template for handling the challenge.

CHAPTER THIRTY ONE

An Industry Unprepared for Growth

I observed this

I n the mid to late 2000s there was a surge in ridership in many western cities, particularly in peak periods. The consequential over crowding led to a deterioration in reliability.

After decades when a constant challenge to O&M Managers was about reducing costs without loss of control of safety or reliability risks there was no clear pathway on how to manage increased demand.

As the various systems struggled to work out how to respond, one key issue became clear: A lack of critical thinking and logic about how to enhance reliable capacity from existing networks and how to develop a case for major new projects and lines.

As a consequence, a series of 'in hindsight' mistakes were made including the publication in Victoria in 2007 of a major rail enhancement plan called Meeting Our Transport Challenges which would be better described as Missing our Transport Challenges.

The ongoing procurement of suburban trains in Perth, Brisbane and London of two door carriages. The impact of two rather than three doors significantly increased station dwell times and their variability which in the short term made reliability worse but in the long term reduced the available number of reliable train slots, or paths.

An exception to this was in Sydney. In this case the Clearways project looked at unlocking more peak hour reliability slots on the existing network by targeting local infrastructure constraints.

The thinking behind this emerged from the successful design and delivery of the Sydney Olympic Train Task where a simplified operating plan enabled very high reliable and very high-capacity services to be provided, when compared to the normal ways of working.

I came to understand that, as a consequence

That an economic based Logic Tree should inform the development and assessment of how to obtain more reliable capacity from the existing network, particularly the most expensive assets, the often underground, tracks and platforms.

Separately, for Major Capacity projects a strategic logic tree framework for developing the case with a particular emphasis on avoiding the often clear but inconvenient unintended consequences of decisions over investment outcomes.

This part of the Book provides both these Logic Tree frameworks. Their validity and logic has been tested in each project resulting in various refinements along the way but has remained essentailly intact since 2008.

Perhaps it's a reflection on me and my shortcomings but I have never seen these documented elsewhere, been trained in them, or had them revealed to me by a Senior Manager or Planner. I hope that they can help you to understand the choices that need to be made.

If I was starting again, I would adopt this approach.

Chapter 32 explains the five step framework for considering the extent to which increasing the latent Network Capacity and Reliability had been exploited without major projects creating new lines and platforms in the core of the network. It seems to have become fashionable for Planners to want to build very expensive new tracks and platforms in city centers without making more use of existing tracks and platforms. This is covered in the next chapter, Chapter 32.

Chapter 33 explains the eight step Major Project Planning Framework as a logic tree guide to avoid making expensive decisions with unfortunate unintended consequences. This is covered in the Chapter 33. Unfortunately, there are many examples of Major Projects starting with step seven of eight with the logic being squeezed in an attempt to create a logic to defend the initial decision.

CHAPTER THIRTY TWO

The Five Step Economic Hierarchy of Increasing Rail Capacity

This five-step hierarchy reflects my experience and is also based on an economic rationale that seeks to maximise the value of the Network Assets. Step One is focused on operating more train paths, using up the latent capacity, before Step Two, getting a higher level of productivity from the train paths.

Step Three reflects a focus on freeing up localised infrastructure constraints to release latent capacity in the Network while Step Four is focused on modernising existing Operating Assets to create much more capacity and value from the existing tracks and platforms, particularly in the City Centers where adding more tracks and platforms is very expensive.

In Melbourne and Sydney there seems to be a reluctance to using this relatively low cost approach, preferring to invest in Step Five, the most expensive option. The selected projects are in the construction phase and are likely to disappoint those who will assess the promised benefits after commissioning. More of that later.

Step One: Run more trains.

- More about frequency than capacity but there are examples.

- In London, for example, despite the huge growth in ridership since the mid 1990s the peak hour timetables in 2018 were remarkably similar to the mid 1980s in the busiest Termini.

Step Two: Run longer trains.

- By adding more Units
- Been a common feature of increasing capacity throughout my career. Examples include
    - Melbourne, Sydney and Perth
    - Thameslink
    - The Windsor Lines

Step Three: Remove local infrastructure bottlenecks.

- A key feature of adding reliable capacity into Sydney and Melbourne since 2000 although some key opportunities have been missed in both Cities unfortunately.

Step Four: Upgrade the Operating Assets.

- Some excellent examples, notably London Underground's Modernisation Programme where some lines have dramatically increased their throughput. The Victoria Line, for example has increased the peak hour throughput from 28 tph to 36.
- Line One in Toronto provides another fine example under the control of the Toronto Transport Commission.
- Sydney Trains' More Trains More Services provides an excellent Australian example too.

Step Five: Build more tracks.

- This is the most expensive way of creating more capacity, certainly in city centers with underground tracks and station. As explained above, the Australian City Transport Planners seem to prefer this than to extract significant additional value form existing Lines, Tunnels and Stations the way that modern metro systems have.

CHAPTER THIRTY THREE

The Eight Steps for planning long term capacity projects

This Framework was developed between 2007 and 2010 whilst working as an Advisor/Facilitator during studies in Melbourne and Sydney.

For decades, in western countries, Rail O&M managers had been building careers concentrating on reducing costs, optimising safety and reliability outcomes along the way for a shrinking industry. Needing to plan and shape rail networks to handle rapid patronage growth was outside generations of experience.

Since 2014 the framework has been refined during assessments and studies in several cities including in Perth in Western Australia and Toronto in Canada.

The Framework attempts to provide a Logic Tree to ensure that Planers and Proponents are forewarned about both the intended and unintended consequences of their choices, before significant expenditure is made.

- **Step One – Consider the future role of road and rail transport in a city in 35 years' time**

  Understand what role the land transport assets are expected to play in the respective city in the future, a minimum of 35 years is useful since the next generation of railway E&M assets are likely to last beyond that time.

Most Transport Agencies are unable to articulate this. They generally make mostly tactical, short term, incremental rather than strategic decisions. Singapore is a notable exception to this

- **Step Two – Identify the end state year and work backwards from it. Do not start from the present.**
Identify the end state, usually at least 35 years into the future.

Every investment and asset renewal, upgrade, obsolescence challenge etc should be managed in this context to avoid the unintended consequence, often expensive.

Understand what the medium to long term outcome is required and ensure every step is a logical step to get there.

Evidence suggest that Rail Planners prefer to adopt a 'starting from here' rather than a 'start from the end and work back' approach. It is easier to work this way and is easier to sell what looks right in today's lens to politicians with short term electoral interests.

The problem with this 'starting from here' approach is that it quickly becomes evident that the chosen solution has wasted significant public funds. The champions of the short-term tactical projects have often moved on by the time the unintended consequences of the shortcomings have revealed themselves.

- **Step Three – What is the predicted peak hour demand in the end-state year at the Heaviest Loading Point (HLP).**
The 'pipe' needs to be able to handle the number of passengers at the HLP, the numbers of people who will want to travel at the busiest time of day, the peak of the peak - it is often less than one hour in the morning.

In the findings of several studies, projected peak hour demand only rarely looks at the future demand at the heaviest loading point, which, in conjunction with the outcomes of Step Four, determine the flow capacity of the 'pipe', the rail line.

In one case a project was based on an end state HLP of 32k passengers per hour, which was then inflated to 38k to help justify the predetermined preferred asset design, before being increased to 54k passengers per hour to eliminate alternative asset design choices to the one that had been selected in the preliminary study. Truly.

- **Step Four – The Customer Service Promise**

What level of comfort is to be promised? Typically, this is about seating, standing time and standing density.

In several studies a key point of interest often presents itself here. In discussions about a future Customer Service Standard regarding standing time and density what emerges is the required future standards being much better than is currently being experienced, specifically about standing time and density. It becomes evident that project proponents are usually not aware of the current customer conditions experienced on a daily basis.

- **Step Five – Develop Operational Plans to meet the step 3 and 4 requirements.**

The options should be based on outcomes that are recognised as being deliverable.

Work in a number of cities suggest that it is normal to develop, and test four options have been provided. There is not a correct answer but there are choices and consequences.

These alternative Concepts of Operation should all provide well considered options for meeting the end state requirements. History shows that the Goodies got it about right, that the alternative solutions are not real alternatives at all. It makes the requirement for Steps Six and Seven redundant.

- **Step Six – Conduct Preliminary Assessments of the Operating Plans**

These assessments should include the following factors to enable the number of Operating Plans to be reduced to a preferred option.

- Financial – capital and O&M costs
- Economic – non-financial benefits
- Constructability
- Operability
- Maintainability

Under Operability, reference should be made to case studies where Systems are successfully functioning to test the feasibility of what is being proposed including frequency, reliability etc. A 'rule of three' for Case Studies is useful to demonstrate practicality and deliverability while avoiding 'bleeding' edge solutions.

- **Step Seven – Identify the asset configuration that each of the Operational Plans require**

Each of the Options requires a different asset base, each with different capex and opex requirements. The selected option becomes the Strategic Operations Plan, the SOP.

- **Step Eight – Identify the asset migration pathway.**

The goal is to get from today to the end state when the SOP is focused on an existing Network, rather than a new, stand-alone Line.

The normal practice, in the absence of the agreed Strategic Operations Plan, is that asset replacement usually involves like for like replacement.

The value of an agreed SOP is that the marginal capex of migrating to a future state requirement is very low, often nothing.

There are three common shortcomings:

Firstly, the lack of proper Options Development, enabling the early concept to emerge as the only sensible alternative.

> Normal Practice resembles The Goodies sketch 'It might as well be string.' There are no real choices provided. In the sketch the dog had three choices: woodchips, razor blades or Nosho's dog food. The marketing men predicted, and were delighted, that the dog chose their new dog food product. Most Major Projects Options Analysis read like this.

Secondly, there is also a propensity to start at Step 7 and then work backwards in an attempt to force the initial idea to emerge as the only sensible choice.

An elaboration on the first point. Planners and proponents start from determining their preferred infrastructure scheme and then force the analysis to win support for the predetermined project.

Sydney, Brisbane, Melbourne and Toronto all provide high profile examples of very expensive, poorly considered new projects.

Thirdly, it has become common in Australia for Government's to publicly commit to multiple billions of dollar projects before any detailed analysis of costs or benefits are developed and evaluated.

Examples of this include the Snowy 2.0 hydro scheme announced in 2017 as a four-year project which reduce electricity process and cost approximately $2bn. A 2022 assessment has found that it is a 10-year project which is likely to cost $10bn and result in increased electricity prices.

The 2022 announced Hells Gate Dam project near Townsville in Queensland at $5.4 bn doesn't even have a business case. The Western Sydney Airport project fists into the same category.

Who is to blame for this?

There is a tendency for senior Rail Leaders to blame their political masters. All but one of eighteen Ministers I have encountered in my career have been open to taking advice.

In Australia the lack of professionalism by many so-called Rail Leaders has allowed many poor value projects to proceed. What does this say about the internal Review and Approval processes within Government? Not much.

CHAPTER THIRTY FOUR

Operational Readiness and the start-up of Major Projects

I observed this...The North East Line, Singapore 2002/03

n November 2001 the Land Transport Authority in Singapore engaged Systra to conduct an assessment of the overall Readiness of the North East Line which at that time was expected to open in September 2002. As part of that review as SBS Transit's Rail Head I was interviewed.

The key question I was asked was, 'On what basis was I going to sign the Declaration of Operational Readiness, the final requirement of the Project Safety Review Process. I thanked the panel for the question and said that I would have a complete answer for their next visit in March 2002 which was not really what they wanted to hear.

In 1999 SMRT had opened the fully automated Bukit Panjang LRT which had many significant problems from very early after opening. The industry consensus was that it hadn't been ready but that a target date was met. An LTA official had said that 'who was I to argue with SMRT, an experienced Operator, once they had signed the Operational Readiness Declaration. Had SMRT been forced to open to meet a predetermined date? I didn't know but what became clear was that the signing, or not of the Declaration could be used as a lever.

By February 2002 we had developed a multi-factor criteria framework identifying the required level of Readiness for the Handover of the Project to start Trial Running with a more demanding criteria for opening for Passenger Service, effectively being reasonably confident that the License Conditions requirements were going to be achievable.

The criteria identified requirements under the following headings:

- Safety, including specific reference to the Hazard Log
- Asset Management including Issues of Concern according to the level of risk
- The status of Operating Rules, Procedures and Work Instructions including Incident and Emergency Readiness Plans
- The Competence of the staff and contractors to perform their duties.
- A Reliability Demonstration Test (RDT) to ensure that the Integrated System worked properly.

The LTA accepted the proposed Framework as being reasonable. So what happened?

The RDT requirement for Trial Running, originally due in mid-2002 was not met until late December 2002 and the RDT Passenger Service Criteria was not met until June 2003.

The start up was regarded as a success even though there were some teething problems. An earlier opening would have led to a repeat of the Bukit Panjang experience with the possible loss of public confidence in the proposed roll out of several fully automated Metro Lines but certainly for SBS Transit with their first venture into the Rail Sector.

The issue that caused the most problems was not with the individual engineering systems themselves but with their integration into a single control system.

I came to understand that, as a consequence

What became apparent was that the criteria framework defined the acceptable end state which had to be met to enable a high-performance outcome. The various Contractors/Suppliers, particularly in the software Control Systems (signalling, communications, trains) all had to collaborate to resolve the complex interface challenges. Without a clear end state, which effectively defined success for the integrated system, arguments about the state and performance of each of the elements of the integrated control system would have gone on for longer.

Who was responsible for the delay? It was never clear except that the integrated system needed to work as one not in their separate parts. It was a single system.

I later read this which reinforced my thinking

In Thameslink, UK it seems incredible that in 2017 the Readiness Board were unaware that the critical inputs into the readiness for Thameslink's opening were unknown by them; Incomplete infrastructure, too few trains, insufficient trained train drivers, unavailability of decision support tools. The operational outcomes were disastrous. A reckless and/or denial approach since the risks were well known to many people. How the Readiness Board didn't seem to know is a different matter.

In a new Metro Line in the late 2010s there was no criteria framework just a date. The ongoing performance difficulties are very similar to those encountered on the Bukit Panjang LRT in 1999/2000 like. Not surprising really.

Mark Wild, the CEO for London's Crossrail project has stated that it is the lack of understanding of the whole of system thinking that has contributed to the four year delay in opening, made much more complex by the procurement of so many different sub systems that need to be integrated into one.

He has spoken of the need for the clear requirements of the end state to be made early in the project so that everything is a step towards achieving it informing both the design and procurement stages of decision making.

This is very much the thrust of the Major Project Concept of Operations options analysis and preferred option selection. All asset procurement decisions should be aimed at enabling an integrated outcome, not being made in isolation from other decisions which is often the case.

If I was starting again, I would adopt this approach

Define the end state acceptance criteria for the Declaration of Operational Readiness early in the Procurement Process to help shape the roadmap on how to get there.

The criteria framework should include the following:

- A Reliability Demonstration Test. Is the service promise going to be delivered?
- The status of Engineering Issues of Concern, particularly those deemed to be required to be fixed before
  - Trial Running and the end of the Project Phase
  - Passenger Services
- The status of the Hazard Log and the closure of all Category A to C hazards with the control measures having been built into the Rules, Procedures and WI with the staff competence assessment covering this.
- The number of fully trained and assessed as competent people in every Department.
- The status of the Operating Rules and Procedures including whether they have been verified through trial with any changes having been promulgated.
- The availability of spares
- The availability of Tools and Test Equipment

References

1. Charles Duhigg: the Power of Habits, 2012
2. Tom Peters: The Excellence Dividend, 2018
3. Jim Collins: Good to Great, 2001
4. James Reason: Managing Organisational Accidents, 1997
5. Turner: Man Made Disasters 1978
6. Ensuring Safety in Britain's Railways: HSE 1993
7. The UK's Safety Case Regulations 1996
8. Diane Vaughan: The Challenger Launch Decision, 1997
9. A World Class Land Transport System, Singapore, 1996
10. Major Accident Inquiries
    a. Zeebrugge Ship Capsize, Belgium. 1987
    b. Kings Cross Fire, London, UK. 1987
    c. Clapham Train Crash, UK. 1998
    d. Piper Alpha Explosion, North Sea, UK. 1989
    e. Newton Train Crash, Scotland. 1991
    f. Ladbroke Grove Train Crash, UK. 1999
    g. Glenbrook Train Crash, NSW 1999
    h. BP Texas Oil Refinery Explosion, USA 2005
    i. Nimrod midair explosion, UK. 2006
    j. Pasir Ris, Singapore, 2016
    k. Salisbury Train Crash, UK, 2020 (Interim Report)
11. UK Health Inquiries
    a. Bristol Infirmary, 2001
    b. Mid Staffordshire, 2013
12. Print Media articles
    a. The Times, UK

b. The Age, Sydney Morning Herald, The Australian and the Herald Sun, Australia

c. The Straits Times, Singapore

ABOUT THE AUTHOR

Simon Lane loved working in various rail teams which have 'made the impossible possible' in terms of safety and reliability in the UK, Australia and Singapore.

Made in the USA
Monee, IL
30 June 2022

98869875R00187